# THE WAY OF AN INVESTIGATOR

# THE WAY OF AN INVESTIGATOR

## A Scientist's Experiences in Medical Research

By

**WALTER BRADFORD CANNON, M.D.**

*George Higginson Professor of Physiology, Emeritus*
*Harvard University Medical School*

(Facsimile of 1945 edition)

HAFNER PUBLISHING COMPANY
New York and London
1965

Originally published 1945
Reprinted 1965

Printed and Published by
Hafner Publishing Company, Inc.
31 East 10th Street
New York, N.Y. 10003

*Printed in U.S.A. by*
NOBLE OFFSET PRINTERS, INC.
NEW YORK 3, N. Y.

WITH GRATITUDE

TO

*C. J. C.*

# CONTENTS

# PREFACE

WILLIAM JAMES set forth the illuminating idea that everybody has as many social selves, or social "me's," as there are distinct persons or groups of persons who see him in a particular role and whose good opinion he specially prizes. As a father, a man reveals an aspect of his nature different from that which he reveals as the member of a profession or as a boon companion in a club; and with his children he enjoys a reputation different from that enjoyed among his fellows.

Admittedly this is a book about one of the me's in my social complex—in the main about me as a scientific worker. More than forty years of my life were spent at the Harvard Medical School in very happy devotion to physiological teaching and research. Persons who have been most influential in forming and maintaining the scientific me have urged that I record some of the consequences, in observations and judgments, which emerged from experiences during that long period.

I confess that the urging met from within a willingness to undertake the task. First, because little is popularly known about the thoughts and doings of men who spend their lives in laboratories trying to discover new facts through carefully devised experiments. It seemed possible that an interest in such topics might be extended and that perhaps my knowledge of investigators and their ways fitted me for telling about them. The range of my research activities on diverse topics and the variety of my associations with colleagues would permit recounting not only my own pursuits but also those of others who have engaged in scientific labor.

It seemed to me also that a sample disclosure of investigative efforts by the investigator himself might be informative. And I had the conviction that enlightenment about the personal phases of scientific discovery could be valuable for science itself, especially in a democratic society. People who have learned about the aims, methods, and achievements of experimenters could be expected to display insight and intelligence in judging scientific endeavor. Furthermore, young persons considering a career to be spent in exploratory scholarship might wish for understanding of its characteristics—its requirements and its rewards. For these different reasons I have written about the motives of the investigator, his problems, his collaborators his various tasks, his mistakes, and his keen satisfactions.

WALTER B. CANNON

Biological Laboratories
*Harvard University*

# CHAPTER I

# AS THE TWIG IS BENT

AN ACCOUNT of formative influences which have affected a career should quite properly start with inheritance. It may not be possible to trace the appearance of many traits from generation to generation through a considerable past—the combinations of determinative factors become too complicated as the numbers in the ancestry multiply. Sometimes, however, the transmission of the infinitesimal hereditary packets in germ cells is demonstrated by peculiar features clearly distinguishable in a long family line. The famous Hapsburg lip is an eminent example. Such evidence justifies looking backward for the appearance of characteristics in some of the forebears, especially in recent history.

Besides biological inheritance there is tradition to be recognized as a potent agency in affecting behavior. The tradition on both my father's and my mother's side was not favorable to a fixed, sessile existence. Both lines were composed of a restless folk, the men and the women ever moving into new ventures. A brief account of the family records will make clear their pioneering habits.

It was about 1700 when there appeared in the small frontier village of Deerfield, Massachusetts, a French Canadian *coureur de bois* named Jacques de Noyon. He was a handy man about the village and in the course of his services he became acquainted with the Stebbins family. The bushranger and one of the Stebbins' daughters, Abigail, fell in love with each other and were married on February 3, 1704. Only a few weeks later French and Indian raiders descended on the village, set fire to its dwellings, killed forty-seven of its inhabitants, and made captives of one hundred and twelve others. The next day the marauders and their prisoners started on the long journey to Montreal through the winter's snow and cold. Jacques de Noyon's acquaintance with the French and the Indians had enabled him to save from the slaughter Abigail's parents and their six children; his knowledge of woodcraft made the hazardous and exhausting travel easier for them.

Many of the Deerfield captives remained in Canada; de Noyon and his wife settled in Boucherville, a village on the south bank of the St. Lawrence River, not far from Montreal. Of their many children the first, René, when about ten years old, was sent with a party of French and Indian traders to visit his grandparents who were back in Deerfield. His grandfather Stebbins persuaded him to stay and when the traders were ready to return, René could not be found. The name René de Noyon had an outlandish sound. Furthermore, the grandfather had previously gone to scriptural sources in naming his own children. He selected Aaron for the little boy, and René de Noyon grew up in Deerfield as Aaron Denio.[1] Such was the origin of the Denio family in the United States. The original name has come down through the generations— one of my great-uncles was an Aaron Denio. My mother was Sarah Wilma Denio.

As generation followed generation the Denios went north through Vermont and then scattered. The line to which I am related moved into the state of New York early in the nineteenth century and thence west to Minnesota and on to Colorado and Wyoming. Always they were early settlers.

On August 4, 1718, five ships sailed into Boston harbor bearing immigrants from Ulster County, Ireland. Some of them

[1] Details of this story are given in Miss Charlotte Alice Baker's *True Stories of New England Captives* (1897) and in *A Genealogy of Aaron Denio of Deerfield, Massachusetts* (1926) by Francis B. Denio D.D., professor in the Bangor Theological Seminary, and Herbert W. Denio, librarian of the Vermont Historical Society.

moved into New Hampshire where the names of Irish towns, Londonderry and Antrim, mark their migration. Others went west in Massachusetts to Hopkinton and later to Blandford in the Berkshire Hills. In the Massachusetts group was Samuel Carnahan, the spelling of whose name was soon simplified to Cannon in accord with the pronunciation. These Scotch-Irish immigrants were the bluest of blue Presbyterians; one of my ancestors was fined four dollars for swimming on Sunday! From Blandford the Cannons, early in the nineteenth century, migrated to Ohio in the settlement of the Western Reserve, and later some of them went on to Wisconsin and Iowa.

One of my great-grandparents, Laura Cochran Cannon, when a girl walked much of the way from Blandford to Aurora, Ohio, beside a covered wagon. Many stories have been told of her pioneer pluck, her good nature, and her unselfish services to the whole community. She once rode alone at night, on horseback, through miles of winter wilderness to secure needed medical aid. It is reported that the extra work done by her in one year included weaving six hundred yards of woolen cloth, one hundred yards of yarn carpet, five blankets and five plaid shawls. She bore eight children and lived to be nearly ninety years old. It is at least pleasant to think that bodily energy is heritable, as has been claimed, and that the group of genes responsible for it have had their way in some of Laura Cochran's descendants.

At Prairie du Chien, a small town on the upper Mississippi River, my father, Colbert Hanchett Cannon, met my mother, who had come from her home at Elba, Minnesota, to teach in a public school. They were married in 1870, and thus the Cannon and Denio lines were brought together.[2] I was born in Prairie du Chien, October 19, 1871. My interest in that historic

[2] Details of the Cannon genealogy and of early conditions in western Massachusetts may be found in *The Descendants of Samuel (Carnahan) Cannon of Ulster, Ireland, and Blandford, Massachusetts,* by Almon Brown Cannon, Wadsworth, Ohio; and in *Ulster Scots and Blandford Scouts* by Sumner Gilbert Wood, West Medway, Massachusetts.

town was intensified in later years when I learned that it contained the site of old Fort Crawford, where in the 1820's the American army surgeon, William Beaumont, "the backwoods physiologist" as Osler called him, made his classic observations on digestion.

At the time of the Civil War my father was in his teens. Because of financial stress he had been compelled to stop his formal schooling and go to work to help support the family, consisting then of his parents and two younger brothers. Throughout most of his life he was connected with western railroads and finally became superintendent of transportation on James J. Hill's Great Northern system. Outside of railroading he cherished two utterly inconsistent interests: a desire to have a small farm, which would have kept him somewhat isolated in the country, and a desire to be a physician, which would have demanded residence in a populous community. He read extensively the literature on both farming and medicine.

My father was ingenious. He invented new methods of keeping records of the movements of cars belonging to the railroad and was instrumental in developing the use of heavy engines to pull long freight trains economically, with little increase in train crews. One of his brothers, who became an engineer, frequently invented clever devices but none of these brought him any considerable financial return. Unfortunately, my father was subject to moods of deep and silent depression. These moods profoundly lowered the morale of his family but he seemed unable to suppress them even if he saw their dark influence on others; indeed, in his gloom he may not have been aware of its effects.

When I was a boy my father refused to buy me ready-made toys. He was himself expert in the use of tools and after giving me some instruction he allowed me free use of an excellent carpenter's tool chest. Occasionally he would work with me in building a small house or other toy structures. I look back upon those times of co-operation as among the happiest memories of my father. The conditions that he provided for developing manual skill proved later to be highly useful, not only in devising laboratory apparatus but also in providing pleasant diversion in making things for the home.

My mother has been described as having an active mind and a quick perception, as being meticulously neat, and extremely modest and unselfish. Highly sensitive, she was easily given to worries and anxieties. I well recall the look of terror on her face when one of my three sisters (all younger than I) became suddenly ill; and again, I remember vividly her consternation when I reported to her that President Garfield had been shot. That was July 2, 1881. About six months later, when I was ten years old, she contracted pneumonia and died. Just before the end she called me to her bedside and said tenderly, "Walter, be good to the world." That wish was most natural for her; it fixed deeply in her son a sacred and haunting memory.

I attended public primary and grammar schools in Milwaukee and St. Paul. In 1888, I entered the St. Paul High School and in three years completed the four-year course. I was older than most of my classmates because my father, convinced that I was not paying proper attention to studies in the grammar school when I was fourteen, had put me at work in a railroad office. There I remained for about two years. The chief value of that experience was a heightened appreciation of the value of free time—even three hours away from work seemed to offer marvelous opportunities. Probably that appreciation had its effect in speeding up my attack on the high-school curriculum. In addition to the routine studies of the high-school course I was for a year editor of the paper, *The High-School World*. At that time Ignatius Donnelly, a local politician and a writer with fantastic imagination, brought out his *Great Cryptogram* designed to prove that Bacon wrote Shakespeare's plays. By use of methods similar to Donnelly's, I found in my Latin Virgil and published in the *World*, pompous pronouncements, one of which was, "Alas, alas, fame is no fun!"

As a boy and as a youth I took pleasure in vigorous sports—

skating, bobsledding, and playing hockey during the winter, and at other times snap-the-whip, pull-away, football, baseball, and tennis. Camping near Minnesota lakes with boyhood friends was another source of outdoor fun; in the camping parties I usually served as cook.

Although my father had had little formal education himself, he desired that his children should enjoy the advantages he had missed. He surrounded us with a good library and provided us with serious magazines, hoping we would profit from them.

During my high-school days Huxley was carrying on his controversy with the Bishop of Peterborough and with Gladstone. These debates I followed with keenest interest, for they disrupted the very strict Calvinistic ideas that had been elaborated in members of the family from early childhood, at church, and in Sunday school. An interest in the foundations of Christian doctrine was at once aroused. I was stimulated to read further and intensively books by John L. Spalding, James Martineau, John Fiske, James Freeman Clarke, and others. Finally my inner turmoil drove me to the confession that I no longer held the views accepted by members of the Congregational church which I had joined. The clergyman in the church, to whom I was sent for counsel, took precisely the wrong course in dealing with my difficulties; he wanted to know what right I had, as a mere youth, to set up my opinion against the opinion of great scholars who supported the church's doctrines. This appeal to authority did not impress me at all, because I knew that there were great scholars in the opposition. Furthermore, I had the feeling that I was entitled to my independent judgment. If I had not been deeply affected by the experience I should simply have shown indifference, and slowly slipped away from my difficulties. Instead, the decision was a source of much distress. Furthermore, my withdrawal from the church resulted in painful friction with my father, who felt that my defection was evidence of his failure to guide and influence me properly. I am pleased to testify that later he was reconciled to my action and took a liberal attitude toward persons who had intellectual differences with him.

The reading of Huxley's controversial articles aroused in me an interest in his essays and also in the writings of Tyndall, Lewes, Clifford, and others whose papers and books on scientific topics were being publicized at the time. This serious reading strongly influenced me in coming to the decision to try to obtain a college education. A graduate of Harvard College, with whom I had become acquainted by chance, attractively presented the advantages offered by his alma mater. There was little money in the family to pay for a college experience in the East, and the University of Minnesota was temptingly near.

My hopes were turned eastward, however, by the suggestions of a woman, Miss M. J. Newson, who had a deep influence on me in my youth. She was an extraordinarily stimulating teacher of English literature in the St. Paul High School. Pupils left her class exercises not only appreciative of niceties of thought and expression, but also stirred to think and discuss. "Is it true that 'Whatever is, is right,' that 'All's well with the world'?" she would ask, and we were off in debate. Her constant sympathy I had received in abundance during my period of intellectual stress. And when I told her about the advice of the Harvard alumnus she urged me strongly to attempt the venture he had suggested. In part through her good offices I succeeded in securing a freshman scholarship; that, together with a small amount of money, about $180 contributed by my father, gave me a start at Harvard. Thereafter, throughout four years of college and four years of the medical course, with the aid of such scholarships as were awarded to me, I earned my way by outside work.

On coming to Harvard College I was suddenly plunged into the new experience of listening to lectures and being required to take notes. At the first lecture I attended, I happened to sit beside a rather badly battered and very ponderous member of the football team. In my ignorance I turned to him for advice, asking him what to put down in my notebook. He growled back *sotto voce,* "Wait till he says something loud. Put that down." It was not long before I learned that, in spite of such expert testimony, there was a great difference between sound and sense.

In the College during the nineties students were allowed to take as many courses as they might wish to carry. In my four years of college life I completed twenty-two courses, and was graduated *summa cum laude* in 1896. Two of the twenty-two courses were of research quality; because of these and also because of graduate courses completed in addition to those required for the A.B. degree, I was granted in 1897, at the end of my first year in the Medical School, the degree of Master of Arts.

The extra courses I took during the four years in college and the outside work in which I engaged in order to meet expenses naturally pressed hard upon available time. There was little opportunity for the amenities of college life. A valuable result of the pressure on time, however, was the discipline it demanded in ways of working. I had to learn to concentrate on the essentials of the task in hand and to finish it rapidly and accurately. This discipline I have regarded as of inestimable value in many later requirements as head of a department and as a leader of research activities.

During my high-school and collegiate studies I was especially interested in the biological sciences. Mathematics was intriguing in its elementary aspects, i.e., through algebra and trigonometry. Unfortunately I did not continue in a study of analytical geometry and calculus. Physics I found not difficult. Descriptive chemistry and analytical chemistry proved attractive, and if I had known the career I was to follow I should have chosen further training in chemical technique. Modern foreign languages were cultivated for practical purposes. Both in high school and in college I derived much intellectual stimulation from independent reading—e.g., Francis Galton's *Inquiries into Human Faculty*—in addition to the routine courses.

My student years in Harvard College were for me exciting.

New ideas were constantly flowering because of contact with stimulating teachers and access to stimulating books and also because of companionship with intellectually eager fellow students, some of whom were in the Graduate School. Among my most influential teachers were Charles B. Davenport, George H. Parker, and William James. With Dr. Davenport I completed my first investigation of a biological phenomenon, the orientation of minute swimming organisms to a source of light. Thus I caught a glimpse of the attractions of scientific research. Dr. Parker, with whom I served as a student assistant for two years shortly after his return from Germany in the early nineties, became later one of my closest friends. His limitless enthusiasm, his beautiful clarity in expounding a subject, and his warm sympathy and understanding of student difficulties and of the earnest aspect of student aims made him an exemplar of admirable qualities which influenced many who had the privilege of coming in contact with him. William James was fascinating in the freshness and constant unexpectedness of his ideas and his phrasing of them. In my eagerness to take much of knowledge as my province I was attracted at one time toward philosophy. I recall walking home with Professor James after one of his lectures and at the end of our talk confessing my inclination toward philosophical studies. He turned on me seriously and remarked, "Don't do it. You will be filling your belly with east wind." The remark probably sprang from his quick recognition of my lack of fitness rather than from his disdain for philosophy. Whatever the reason for his advice, I followed it.

At the beginning of the last of my four years at the Harvard Medical School I was invited to conduct at Harvard College and at Radcliffe College the course in comparative anatomy of vertebrates, in which I had been student assistant while an undergraduate. At the end of the year, in June, 1900, when I received the M.D. degree, offers came to me of a continuing instructorship in zoology in Cambridge and an instructorship in physiology at the Medical School in Boston. I decided to accept the latter. For two years (1900 until 1902) I had the title of instructor; for four years thereafter (1902-1906) I was assistant professor; and in 1906 I was appointed successor to Henry P. Bowditch, as George Higginson Professor of Physiology, an appointment which continued until my resignation in August, 1942. The thirty-five years during which Dr. Bowditch held the chair of physiology in the Medical School and the thirty-six years during which I held it covered the entire period of the development of physiology as an actively pursued medical science in the United States. Before 1871 it was a subject presented to the students in textbooks and in lectures commonly given by professors of medicine under the title "institutes of medicine."

A year after graduating from the Medical School I was married to Cornelia James. We had known each other as students in the St. Paul High School, and our friendship grew in intimacy while she was an undergraduate at Radcliffe and I was studying at the Harvard Medical School. When our wedding was announced in the department of physiology one of the staff at that time quoted regretfully, "A young man married is a young man marred." This is a cynical dictum I cannot confirm. Throughout our married life my wife has been my best, my most helpful and most devoted counselor and companion.

When I was a boy my father had expressed a wish that I might become a doctor. Somewhat vaguely I had that intent when I entered Harvard College. It was not until I had passed about halfway through the college period and had studied chemistry and biology to a considerable degree that the resolution became definitely formulated. At that time I was attracted by the possibility of devoting my life to neurology and psychiatry. With this aim I undertook work on the structure of the brain and in psychology. While in the Medical School I paid special attention to courses concerned with diseases of the nervous system. It is probable that if, while a first-year student of medicine, I had not undertaken research on the physiology of the digestive tract by use of the then newly discovered X-rays, I would have become a neurologist.

My father's wish that I might become a physician was therefore never realized. Instead of engaging in practice I engaged in teaching medical students. This was what my predecessor, Dr. Bowditch, had done. He told the tale of a conversation between one of his children and a little companion. The companion asked, "Has your father many patients?" and the answer was, "He has no patients." "What! A doctor and no patients?" Thereupon the apologetic answer, "Oh, no, he is one of those doctors who don't know anything!" Possibly the children of other physiologists suffer from the same sense of inferiority. One of my daughters, on being informed proudly by a little friend that *her* father was a doctor, remarked somewhat sadly, "*My* father is only a father."

Elsewhere in this volume I have traced the sequential development of the researches which my collaborators and I have conducted during the more than four decades of my experience as an investigator. There is no need for anticipating here the record of that development. It may be pertinent to remark, however, that at every stage there were numerous fresh ideas which suggested the next stage of research to be undertaken— from an interest in digestive functions, through studies of emotional effects on bodily processes, to regulation of steady states in the body and the chemical mediation of nerve impulses. In this onward movement of interests innumerable problems were left unsolved. Indeed, the forward look to the exploration of enticing fresh vistas, which the preliminary studies had revealed, was so attractive that neglect of the old in order to attend to the new seemed imperative. Fortunately the unanswered questions left behind were noted by other physiologists and became the occasion for their researches. This mode of spreading one's influence is one of the incidental satisfactions that the investigator can enjoy.

# CHAPTER II

# THE SPIRIT OF ADVENTURE

INVESTIGATORS do not march straight to their goal with ease and directness. In their imagination they see a possible fact and they set forth to learn whether their foresight can be realized. Or they come upon something which is puzzling and challenging and which they wish to explain; then they try in various ways to relate it to other phenomena that would solve the riddle. Obstacles and difficulties are sure to be encountered. The search for understanding is an adventure or, more commonly, a series of adventures. If an attempt in one direction fails, the failure is not discouraging to an eager explorer. There are other possible approaches to the end in view and relentlessly, one after another, these are tried. When the goal is reached, there is occasion for joy and exultation. A conquest has been achieved. New knowledge has been gained which deeply satisfies both the explorer's adventurous spirit and his persistent curiosity.

Long before experimental methods of advancing knowledge began to enthrall investigators in science, venturesome men found their satisfactions in geographical excursions. They crossed uncharted oceans; they wandered over unmapped territory. But such possibilities have largely disappeared. Untrodden places on the earth are now rare. In the United States a progressive civilization has long since obliterated our rugged frontiers. In the world itself both poles have been visited. Everest has been nearly conquered, and in almost all ranges the nooks and crannies of continents have been examined. The thrill of being first to find a spot which has not before been reached and to view it "with a wild surmise" is quite exceptional. The happy fortune of enjoying such an event befell my wife and myself on our wedding journey. Since the adventure gives me an opportunity to compare the motives and the experiences of explorers of the earth and investigators in laboratories of scientific research, the story is worth telling.

We had been married about three weeks. During that time we had paddled, in an Indian birchbark canoe, down the historic St. Croix River (part of the western boundary of Wisconsin) and thence for about sixty miles along the broad Mississippi between its impressive bluffs. Twice we were reported as Indians and finally we were regarded as harvest hands looking for jobs! Then, brown and toughened by the hard work of propelling our heavily laden craft and making and breaking camp in a daily round, we were ready for fresh adventures. We boarded a train for northwestern Montana. The particular region we sought was a United States forest reserve; it is now well known as Glacier National Park. Shortly after our arrival at the foot of Lake MacDonald we learned from a local guide and hunter, Charlie Howe, gaunt and picturesque in his fringed buckskins, that he was going to the far end of the lake that day in a little steam launch. That was a chance; we decided to go with him. As we looked toward our destination we saw, standing out boldly at the head of the lake, an impressive mass called Goat Mountain, which the guide declared had never been climbed. At once the idea occurred to us that it would be a novel sort of enterprise if we should attempt to reach the peak which rose before us.

A French-Canadian squatter named Comeau was willing to let us have horses to take us along an old Indian trail to the base of the mountain and, further, he agreed to accompany us. Photographs of the mountain bring out clearly its general features. A rather steep rise of perhaps eight hundred feet, bearing trees and bushes, merges into a more gradual slope of several thousand feet, practically bare of vegetation. At the top of this slope is an almost vertical wall reaching around the great mass like a collar. Winter pictures reveal this wall as being so vertical as not to hold the snow. From the top of the wall there is another gradual slope rising to a rocky citadel which caps the immense bulk below.

At daybreak, July 17, 1901, refreshed by a night's sleep under giant pines, we started the climb. After an arduous and exacting struggle—there were no trails—at about ten o'clock we reached the base of the vertical wall. There we found a well-worn path evidently trodden by the mountain goats, for occasionally on the stiff shrubs along the way we saw bits of their white fleece which had been caught and pulled off. As we followed the path, looking for a place where the wall could be scaled, we were much chagrined to find tied to a shrub a bit of cloth. Obviously someone had been there before us, and fairly recently.

At last the path led us to a sloping crevice in the wall. The upper and the nether sides of the crevice seemed sufficiently far apart to permit us to crawl between them to the top. Comeau, who was slight, succeeded in doing this. My wife likewise was successful. Then I started up. My narrowest diameter, however, proved too great for a spot where the crevice narrowed. I was stuck, and in a desperate plight. I could not advance nor could I look down to find where I might have a safe lower footing. To add to my distress I saw a folding tin cup, which was forced out of my pocket as I squirmed, go bounding down the smooth rocky slope for hundreds of feet. By good fortune at last I felt a small ledge where my hobnails would hold. Thereby I worked my way free from the wedged position and regained the path below. As I sat on it, I experienced an emotional reaction which appeared suddenly and mysteriously and deeply stirred my scientific curiosity. My body was shaking violently as in a chill—shaking like an "ashpan" as an old negro put it. There was nothing for the others to do but to slip down the crevice and join me.

Now we resumed our tramp along the path. It became smaller as it rose on the face of the wall until it was only a dangerously narrow shelf, with the wall on one side and the bare mountainside on the other. We took pains not to look down that slope. Fortunately, as we continuously crept along the shelf, we soon arrived at a place in the wall where water from the snow above had repeatedly frozen and melted and thus had broken the rock. There it was possible to make our way up over the wet, fragmented surface until we reached the highest slope.

Now we had come to a region where even the goats had not ventured. Every step we took sent loose crumbled rock sliding downward. In the circumstances climbing was extremely difficult, for every step upward was largely lost as the stones slipped downward beneath our weight. Nevertheless, after arduous efforts, we managed to reach the base of the crowning citadel and to clamber to the top.

The glory of the view disclosed to us was hardly to be imagined. The mountain we had scaled, situated slightly west of the main range of the Rockies, allowed us to look away north and south for perhaps a hundred visible miles in either direction. The snow-capped peaks, the glaciers, the lakes, the waterfalls, all were gleaming in the sunshine. To the north rose the steep sides of the Garden Wall. To the east we could see the vast Montana plain spreading away from the base of the mountains, like a gray-green carpet. Later we learned that we were at the very crest of the continent. St. Mary's Lake was partly visible, itself a source of the Missouri River and connecting thus with the Mississippi system and the Gulf of Mexico. A score of miles northward was an area draining into the Saskatchewan and so into Hudson Bay. And west of us was a stream whose waters entered Lake MacDonald and flowed thence to the Columbia and the Pacific Ocean.

That we might leave evidence of our climb we wrote on a scrap of paper a brief account of it and the date, and put the record in a small bottle. Over it we built a cairn of flat stones. So far as we are aware, no one has climbed the mountain since that time. It is quite possible that through the intervening decades the paper has disintegrated. The cairn should be there, however, and the bottle under it.

It was nearly three o'clock in the afternoon when we realized that if we were to return to our camping place before dark, we must shut our eyes to the glories all around us and start downward. On our way we had an adventure that might have proved disastrous. At a hollow place below the wall, where snow had gathered and was melting, we stopped to have a drink of water and to eat some sandwiches. As we sat there, tired but carefree, we heard an ominous roar above us.

Comeau sprang to his feet and shouted, "Run for the side! Run for the side!" Above the hollow where we had been sitting there was a depression in the height of the wall. As we dashed to the side of the hollow, we saw a huge rock come rolling off the top of the mountain's parapet, land ponderously with a tremendous crash, and go bounding down the thousands of feet of bare slope. It was followed by a continuous stream of small stones which poured on the very spot where we had been eating our lunch.

Dusk was upon us as we arrived back at camp, tattered and torn and well-nigh exhausted. In the morning we were awakened by a horseman riding along the trail and leading a string of pack animals. He explained that he was a packer serving a topographical party that was mapping the region for the United States Geological Survey. We told him we were there because the day before we had gone to the top of Goat Mountain. He said that members of the party had tried to reach the top a few weeks previously, but had been blocked by a vertical wall they encountered. Thus was explained the bit of cloth we found beside the path in our climb. The packer asked us our name, which we wrote down for him.[1]

Seven years later we were invited to dine with a colleague in the Harvard Department of Geology. At the dinner we were

---

[1] A letter written shortly after our return to civilization, to tell our parents about our adventure, was found many years later and published in the *Park Service Bulletin*, IX (1939), 37-40.

introduced to Mr. François E. Matthes of the United States Geological Survey, a topographer. When asked where he had worked, he mentioned among other places northwestern Montana. And when? "1901." Thereupon I informed him that in 1901 my wife and I had climbed a mountain at the northern end of Lake MacDonald. A few days later the mail brought a beautiful contour map of the area of Glacier National Park, and there, at the head of the lake, was Mt. Cannon. Because there were two Goat Mountains in the region another name for one of them had to be found, and the government had given our name to the one which we had been first to climb.

To expert mountaineers who have scaled the Matterhorn or Mt. McKinley or other dangerous and difficult peaks, our small achievement will seem trifling. Going up to about ten thousand feet through such hazards as we encountered was for us, however, a thrilling adventure. And it included some prominent features of adventure in scientific investigation—the vision of what is desired, the opportunity to try to gain it, the strenuous effort, the signs of previous explorers, the incidence of unanticipated experiences, the encountering of impassable obstacles and the shift to other approaches, and at last the reward of reaching the goal and beholding a revelation of exciting fresh aspects of nature.

Now that geographical boundaries in our own and in other civilized lands have been determined, the pioneering spirit finds in scientific research enticing vistas for adventure. The twilight zone between what we know and the vast unlimited range of what we do not know presents us with innumerable frontiers. In this zone the opportunities for novel experiences are immensely more abundant than they have ever been in the long history of explorations on land and sea. If any one remains for a brief time in an active laboratory of experimental research he is sure soon to be shown phenomena never previously observed. Here again is true pioneering. As in the early days, it imposes on the adventurer who wishes to become an explorer certain demands. What are they?

First among them is resourcefulness. The experimenter tries to imagine conditions that may be encountered; he may not meet them at all, but he may meet others he had not anticipated. New devices may be required to overcome unforeseen difficulties. As the frontiersman may make a corn knife out of a broken scythe blade, or a butcher knife out of a rusty file, or a soap factory from an empty barrel and an iron kettle, so the pioneering investigator may be compelled to use his ingenuity to the limit in adapting available apparatus and materials to the purposes he has in mind.

Another requisite is a forward look and a faith in the efficacy of present and future efforts. We in the United States have associated the optimistic frontiersman with the advancing boundary of our civilization in the settlement of the West. In one of his essays Samuel Crothers remarked that there was no fixed line between the East and the West—it lay where the look changed from day-before-yesterday to day-after-tomorrow. In laboratories where experiments are going on, the hopeful "prospect" of the pioneer is still a prime motive. It is related to a characteristic pioneering attitude of the investigator—an unwillingness to be satisfied with what is already known. As Daniel Boone moved onward whenever he could see smoke rising from a chimney, so the worker in science advances toward novel realms of experience. A driving initiative compels him to seek new ventures. When they have yielded the satisfactions of discovery they become achievements of the past, to be left behind while he enters on further quests.

The boundary of knowledge, however, is pushed forward with painful slowness, and always, as an advance is achieved, further territory to be explored is revealed. We may feel grateful that the attractions, the excitements, and the satisfactions of pioneering are still provided in the realm of scientific investigation.

Beaumont, conducting his physiological researches at Fort

Crawford during the first decades of the last century, affords a good example of the frontiersman in two senses. He was an American army surgeon; he nursed to health and for years took care of a Canadian hunter, Alexis St. Martin, whose stomach had been permanently opened by an accidental gunshot wound. This remarkable chance occurrence made possible an exploration of digestive processes in the stomach, at will, in many different circumstances. In admirably careful observations on his famous patient Beaumont performed experiments which made history in science.

Fort Crawford, at that time, was surrounded by a straggling village with a nondescript population of Indians, French traders and trappers, half-breeds, and a few American settlers. The doctor worked, therefore, in the fringe of settlements whose westward movement was one of the most romantic aspects of our country's history; but he himself was traveling quite alone in his search for new knowledge. He had full faith in the importance of the scientific work in which he was engaged, and of its permanent value. Though old Fort Crawford on the upper Mississippi has vanished, the results of the experiments Beaumont conducted within its walls have come down to us with undiminished luster through more than a hundred years and are an enduring portion of America's gifts to science. "Truth, like beauty," Beaumont wrote, "when 'unadorned is adorned the most,' and in prosecuting these experiments and inquiries I believe I have been guided by its light." Such is the ideal and such is the faith of the frontiersman in science, and in so far as he is loyal to his convictions he will leave behind him, as Beaumont did in his records, lasting contributions from his fleeting years.

Being venturesome involves taking risks. The risks will vary with different disciplines. Chemists have been killed or seriously maimed in their efforts to discover new kinds of explosives. Bacteriologists have been rendered desperately ill or have died from diseases for which they have been endeavoring to find a cure. Workers with the X-rays, in the early days be-

fore the dangers were realized, lost the use of fingers and hands
or became horribly mutilated by the destructive energy of that
powerful agent. In other realms of research the dangers may
not be so serious, but all research is fairly certain to involve at
least the regrettable risk of losing time. "Uncertainty and loss
of time," as Emerson wrote, "are the nettles and tangling vines
of the self-relying and the self-directed." Since time runs in only
one direction, the eager investigator always looks upon its loss
with sorrow. In my own experience I have too often had only
labor for my pains. If the time I have spent in fruitless efforts
to obtain control of the workings of the thyroid gland could
be added to the end of my days, my span of life would be prolonged, I feel sure, by some years.

Experience in the adventures of research is likely to impress
on the investigator the habit of accepting the incidents of life
in a pioneering spirit. Events as they occur are met with an understanding that they too can be adventures. Unpleasant incidents call for resourcefulness in order to avoid their consequences. Time-consuming accidents come to be received with
equanimity, even if tinged with sadness. Risks are run with a
serene recognition that they may end unfavorably. And hope is
held high that, in the future, conditions will improve. I do not
claim that these habits are established in all investigators or
that they are invariably in supreme control!

During my long experience in a busy laboratory I have had
many opportunities to note the conditions which affect the research spirit, the characteristics of productive experimenters
and their ways of working, the mistakes of novices and the errors of experts, the harm and the value of controversies, and
other aspects of the life of the investigator. In the following
chapters I shall try to take the reader behind the scenes and
let him know what occurs there.

# CHAPTER III

# FITNESS FOR THE ENTERPRISE

As THE years have gone by, I have been more and more impressed by the occasional lack of one or another of the essential qualities in a man, that spoils his otherwise excellent equipment in mind and character. As an investigator he may, for example, be rich in suggestive ideas and yet be indolent and therefore sterile; he may be a hard worker but secretive about his results and suspicious of his fellow workers, so that he is despised by them; he may be an earnest experimenter but inconsiderate of his helpers, and therefore he may find that help is begrudged him; or he may be prone to display an attitude of superiority and consequently be subjected to derision, expressed or silent. Sometimes an investigator's excellence in important regards is so great that it overbalances his defects. I have heard of an eminent scientist who, after weeks of intense and exhausting labor on a difficult problem, would break away in a disgraceful carouse. His escapades were tolerated because of his outstanding discoveries. Clearly such need for balancing good and evil is not to be looked upon with any enthusiasm. It is better to strive for a set of qualities that can consistently exist in one another's companionship and that together favor effectiveness.

Curiosity has been condemned as a disease and as a low vice, and theologians and poets have solemnly warned against it. But in spite of the testimony that it was curiosity which lost us Paradise, I am sure that all who are aware of the fruits of the Tree of Knowledge would agree that they have become abundant because of the spying and trying of inquisitive scientists. The New

England expletive, "I want to know!" expresses in the investigator a persistent passion. He sees events and changes in his field which seem to him strange and mysterious. Instead of ignoring them, as most people do, he wonders about them and sets to work to learn their characteristics. Curiosity is the mainspring of his initiative and his persistent industry. It is a prime requisite for a career of exploration.

In general, I would point out that there are two ways open for us to obtain knowledge of nature's secrets. We may merely watch natural events as they occur or we may arrange conditions so that the events will appear, disappear, or be modified as we may decide. For example, the growth of wheat may be studied carefully in different native surroundings or, on the other hand, the wheat may be grown where the effects on it of heat and cold, sunlight and darkness, wind, gravity, drought, and the chemicals of the soil can be examined individually as these various agencies affect its growth and productiveness. The former method is purely observational, the latter is experimental. The experimental method, in which the conditions to be observed are held under control, is in the main the distinguishing feature of modern science.

Contrary to popular belief, there is nothing magical about science. The scientific method implies first that study of natural events suggests certain explanations for their occurrence as, for example, that lime in the soil or high temperature makes hard wheat. The inquiring person, instead of immediately accepting suggested explanations as true, prefers to put them to test.

Of the two ways of learning about nature, experiments have proved much more fruitful than simple observations—chiefly, I think, because experimentation is addressed more directly to the means of controlling natural forces.

Inquiry into the conditions which lie back of phenomena and which determine their appearance calls for imaginative insight and the projection of an idea as to what the conditions may be. The investigator works on the possibility of realizing an idea.

It is pertinent to note that he thereby shares the qualities of poets and artists, who exercise the gifts of penetrating insight and creative interpretation. The proposed explanation must, of course, be very thoughtfully considered, with regard both to other possible explanations and to what has been previously learned. In order to make progress it is highly important, as in the fairy tale, to "ask the proper question."

Imagination serves an important purpose both in designing an experimental study and later when freshly discovered facts demand an interpretation. At both stages a questioning attitude should balance imaginative enthusiasm. Critical queries should be posed at both stages. In drawing inferences alternative possibilities should be scrupulously noted and thoughtfully considered. And all inferences should be carefully checked to make sure that they do not reach beyond the point which the facts justify.

President Eliot of Harvard enjoyed telling the story of an experience he once had, illustrating proper caution in drawing a conclusion. When he entered a crowded New York restaurant, he handed his hat to the colored doorman. As he came out he was astonished to see the doorman promptly pick his hat out of the hundreds there and hand it to him. In his surprise he asked, "How did you know that was my hat?" "I didn't know it was yo' hat, suh," was the answer. "Why, then," asked Mr. Eliot, "did you hand it to me?" Very courteously the doorman replied, "Because you handed it to me, suh." This precise limitation of inference pleased the president.

There is likely to be a conflict between imaginative enthusiasm and a proper critical attitude toward a problem and the means of solving it. I have known investigators who were so extremely critical of possibilities that they remained almost unproductive; they were so constantly seeing obstacles in their way, and difficulties of interpretation if one or other result might follow from an experimental test, that they hesitated to undertake commitment of their time to the inquiry. On the other hand, the imagination, if not critically controlled, may lead an investigator into ill-considered ventures which will waste his time or into wild speculations which damage his reputation as a considerate man of science.

A favorable condition for productivity in research is variety of experience, both one's own experience and that which may be derived through observation of others who are at work on different problems. Especially is this important during the early years of education and discipline. Thus insight into diverse methods is acquired, as well as acquaintance with ways in which they are applied. As an investigator continues in his career, accident will present him with unpredicted opportunities for research, perhaps in quite new directions. The early knowledge of various ways of solving problems provides him promptly with readiness and versatility of attack.

Investigators are commonly said to be engaged in a search for the truth. I think they themselves would usually state their aims less pretentiously. What the experimenter is really trying to do is to learn whether facts can be established which will be recognized as facts by others and which will support some theory that in imagination he has projected. But he must be ingenuously honest. He must face facts as they arise in the course of experimental procedure, whether they are favorable to his idea or not. In doing this he must be ready to surrender his theory at any time if the facts are adverse to it. The tragedy of scientific inquiry, as Huxley once remarked, is "the slaying of a beautiful hypothesis by an ugly fact."

Technical skill in physiological and in other biological experimentation may involve a knowledge of the procedures of modern surgery. This means an acquaintance with the methods of surgical anesthesia, with the precautions necessary to avoid infection, and with the use of surgical instruments, as well as a knowledge of the attentions to aftercare during convalescence.

The experimental method requires ingenuity and skill in contriving appropriate devices for securing the evidence needed to learn whether an idea is valid or not. Acquaintance with the use of tools and with various materials is highly valuable where physical tests are to be applied. My own boyhood experience with a carpenter's equipment has, as I have already noted, proved very useful. For different types of experimental work different ingenuities of technique are desirable. In chemical research, for example, knowledge of ways in which substances combine and reactions take place is of primary importance. In a physiological laboratory there was a time when apparatus could be made of cork and wire and wax. Today, however, the common employment of electrical methods, both to stimulate structures into activity and to record accurately their responses to stimulation, demands a thorough familiarity with electrical instruments and the ways in which they operate.

The investigator in biological science should have, besides a knowledge of electrical apparatus and its uses, a good grounding in other aspects of physics and also in chemistry. These fundamental sciences are so intimately involved in biological phenomena that, according to some theorists, biophysics and biochemistry constitute the whole of biology. And since the ideal of quantitative measurement has been to a great degree reached in both physics and chemistry, that ideal is held as the essential aim in biological investigations. No one will gainsay the desirability of precise statement and accurate analysis and, in some circumstances, of mathematical treatment of observations. A knowledge of the applications of mathematics—especially a knowledge of statistical methods—is a valuable adjunct to the biologist's mental equipment.

This does not mean that, at present, biological phenomena in general can be subjected to mathematical manipulation. Some of these phenomena involve a complexity which makes impossible such interpretation as the physicist, for example, applies to his problems. Even in physics the experimental method by itself has proved marvelously revealing. Faraday testified, "It is quite comfortable to me to find that experiment need not quail before mathematics, but is quite competent to rival it in discovery." The biologist should not be looked upon with disdain because his studies are sometimes not quantitative in method. Such intellectual snobbishness is not warranted so long as there are highly important fields of investigation to which mathematics, as a mode of expression, is not applicable. It is a satisfaction to know that the eminent physical chemist, G. N. Lewis, has declared, "I have no patience with attempts to identify science with measurement, which is but one of its tools, or with any definition of the scientist that would exclude a Darwin, a Pasteur, or a Kekule." To those three may be added Harvey, Virchow, Pavlov, Sherrington and many others.

The investigator should not only possess but also train himself in keen powers of observation. He should be alert and watchful as events transpire in the course of experiments, so that nothing escapes his vigilance. We readily behold the familiar; we may overlook the unfamiliar. An old saying has it: "We are prone to see what lies behind our eyes rather than what appears before them." Especially when recording devices are employed should the experimenter be on his guard. The record may reveal minor variations and if the accompaniments of these variations are not noted at the time, they remain unexplained. Thus a new phenomenon may be quite overlooked. There should never be complete and exclusive dependence on any artificial device for registering biological processes.

A retentive and facile memory is a highly important qualification. Remembered facts are the very stuff ideas are made of, the stuff used by a creative imagination, or by a happy accident, or by a surprising flash of insight, to furnish new vistas of possible progress.

An illuminating instance of the value of memory occurred during our Harvard researches on acetylcholine, a chemical agent which appears at the ends of nerves when they are active and which can cause the governed muscle to contract. If the nerve is stimulated rapidly for some time signs of extreme fatigue appear: the muscle no longer responds. We know that the nerve itself does not become tired, nor does the muscle, to a marked degree. The failure of response is now explained as being due to such reduction of the acetylcholine at the nerve terminals that the muscle is no longer excited into contraction. Curiously, an Indian arrow poison, curare, paralyzes contraction by blocking the influence of the agent on the muscle, though it does not prevent discharge of the agent from the nerve endings. In these circumstances, therefore, it could be quite possible, by continuous and prolonged stimulation of nerves governing muscles, to exhaust the supply of acetylcholine while the muscle remains quite inactive behind the barricade set up by curare. I happened to recall that Bowditch (about sixty years before) had performed the experiment of administering curare, then for hours exciting the motor nerve of a muscle, and finally observing, as the influence of curare disappeared, that the muscle responded well to the nerve stimulation by contracting. Here was evidence that exhaustion had not occurred. How could this extraordinary event be explained? What did it imply? My associates then repeated the experiment of stimulating a muscle through its nerve until fatigue appeared and the muscle ceased to contract. That was the point at which, previously, investigators had supposed that the end had been reached. Now, however, the stimulation was continued, and to the amazement of all of us in the laboratory the muscle began to contract again. Gradually its response increased and continued increasing, apparently without any sign of fatigue, until it was performing nearly as well as it did initially. The acetylcholine was obviously being produced again after it had disappeared. A new fact had emerged. It seems not improbable that this remarkable reappearance of persistent muscular activity after extreme fatigue may play a role in developing the strange phenomenon of second wind.

Patience is another quality the investigator needs. As he enters unexplored territory, he may encounter a veritable jungle of hindrances and complications. Results which he had good reason to expect to find promptly may not be disclosed or they may be so incongruous that they bewilder him. The question then arises whether to push onward or to give up the attempt. Sometimes his method, when carefully examined, is found to be defective. If the method is not at fault, the difficulty may be due to elements in the conditions he is investigating that he has not taken into consideration. Obstacles encountered in research, however, sometimes yield quite as important results as those which were anticipated. In 1897, when I was using the recently discovered X-rays in studying the movements of the stomach, I was greatly disconcerted by occasional interference with my observations. Although some animals displayed the rolling waves of the stomach wall with the utmost definiteness, others showed no movements whatever. The whole purpose of my effort, of course, was to see the waves and to learn their effects. Their failure to appear in animals which had been carefully prepared was a serious check on my progress. Only after some time did I note that the absence of activity was accompanied by signs of perturbation and that when serenity was restored the waves promptly reappeared. This observation, a gift for my troubles, led to a long series of studies on the effects of strong emotions on the body.

In the complex circumstances of a scientific inquiry there is always the possibility that what has been imagined is quite incapable of proof or that it may be too difficult to prove by the means available. While patience and tenacity in research are admirable, a situation may arise in which persistence is unwarranted. Then these admirable qualities may become mere obstinacy. As I have previously confessed, I have spent unconscionable time in trying to obtain control of the secretion from the thyroid gland. I fear that something less admirable than steadfastness was manifested in that endeavor.

When in the course of a research an investigator has run into a blind alley, he should keep a record of it and in a later report he should note briefly the effort that has proved to be futile. Experience obtained in an unsuccessful excursion may thus become valuable to other explorers traveling the same path. Knowledge is advanced largely by the method of trial and error and, if false steps which have been taken are not recorded, they are likely to be repeated.

Willingness to take infinite pains and to regard carefully minute details is an essential element of the research spirit. Astronomy and physics afford many examples of great discoveries that have followed from noting slight and unobtrusive irregularities. Only by paying attention to a minor deviation in the orbit of Uranus did Adams and Leverrier, independently, calculate the existence of the planet Neptune. When Cavendish combined atmospheric nitrogen with oxygen by electric sparking, there remained in the chamber a trace—less than 1 per cent— of an unknown gas. He recorded the fact, however, and a hundred years later Rayleigh, repeating the experiment, found in the residue a new element which he named argon; it is now used as an inert atmosphere in electric light bulbs. Furthermore, the small recorded remnant led Ramsay to demonstrate in the ordinary air a series of indolent elementary gases, among them neon, which we see everywhere employed in the orange-red lights of commercial signs. Again, detection of otherwise unexplained lines in the solar spectrum resulted in the discovery of helium, as traces in the air and as a constituent of natural gas. Such are instances of the value of painstaking attention to small discrepancies and the faithful recording of their existence.

Although there are noteworthy examples of eminent scientific achievement by men who were of frail physique—Darwin, for example—it is easy to see that vigorous health is a great advantage in research as in other activities. Perhaps it is especially valuable for the investigator, because he is subject to conditions which may make extreme demands upon his physical strength and his resistance to disease. If he is studying infections, for example, he runs the risk of being infected himself, as Zinsser was; and even if he is in good health he may succumb, as did Rickett and Noguchi. When the trail is hot and new results of high significance are being frequently disclosed, the investigator may work himself to exhaustion. He spends not only laborious days but also laborious nights, and has but scant time for meals. One of my students frequently followed an experiment all day and onward to its conclusion at three or four o'clock in the morning. Only a stalwart man can for long endure such stresses.

While no amount of learning will provide a man who lacks them with those inborn qualities of imagination and enterprise which make for productive scholarship, it is clear that the experimental investigator should be a person of broad education. He should not only know the past of his own science—what has been achieved by others in the special field in which he is working, what his contemporaries are doing, and the varieties of methods that can be brought to bear in solving the problems he has set himself—but he should also be informed about other sciences. In addition, he should have some knowledge of foreign tongues, and should be able to write well in his own.

Active scientific investigation is going on in many countries, and the results are published in the national languages. In the past, most of the scientific records have been reported in German, French, and Italian, one or the other of these languages having commonly been used in publications from Russia, from Japan, from the Spanish-speaking and the Scandinavian countries, and from Holland. The advantages of being able to read an article, especially one reporting work closely related to that of the investigator, in the original language, are obvious.

It is essential that a scientific observer should be able to write a clear and definite report of his aims, his methods, his results, and his conclusions. Flowery language and dramatization are out of place in scientific exposition. Likewise the art of persuasion—i.e., special pleading—must be excluded, for the facts presented should be convincing without an appeal to feelings. The prime requirements are clarity and brevity. In view of the enormous volume of scientific publication, I would like to emphasize brevity.

The clarity and brevity which are so necessary will both be well served if the writer exercises care in his selection of words and phrases. Precision in the use of descriptive terms is highly desirable and often provides a memorable fillip because of its striking pertinence. And the charm of an imaginative phrase is hauntingly persistent. The English physiologist, Sir Joseph Barcroft, is a master of such scientific writing. Who would ever forget his testimony that the suffusion of warmth which spread over his body, when he had exposed himself, naked, to a frigid atmosphere, made him feel as if "basking in the cold"? The art of finding words which nicely fit the thought and which also are piquantly picturesque is rare. It is an art not easy to achieve, but we can admire it and strive for it.

Desire to give due credit to earlier investigators in the field which he is extending often presents the scientific writer with a dilemma. Descriptions of previous studies consume print and paper and human labor, and crowd library shelves. On the other hand, credit should be assigned where it is warranted, for otherwise the reader may not know the antecedents of the immediate enterprise and the workers who have contributed to it, and he may therefore fail to understand the relative importance of the discoveries being reported. Not infrequently this dilemma can be solved by reference to summarizing articles in previous publications to which, in all fairness, the attention of the reader can be directed. In such circumstances it is not necessary to introduce the account of a research by an elaborate historical preamble; citations mav be limited to those most directly pertinent.

The investigator should be generous toward his fellow scientists. Generosity may be expressed in one respect by not rushing into another's field the moment it is opened. The successful explorer who has made startling progress in a novel enterprise should be given an opportunity to expand his discoveries without being crowded by newcomers. Another opportunity for generosity is provided in repeating the work of others. Sometimes experiments are performed that lead to criticism of fellow investigators when in fact care has not been taken to repeat exactly the methods and the conditions originally employed. Many years ago observations were made in the Harvard Physiological Laboratory on the rate of discharge of different foodstuffs from the stomach. Standard quantities, having uniform consistency, were mixed with bismuth subnitrate and fed. By means of the X-rays, and under wholly normal conditions, it was shown that starchy food is discharged from the stomach rapidly, fat food very slowly, and protein food at an intermediate rate. In explanation of these different rates a theory was propounded as to the way in which acid in the gastric juice might govern the exit from the stomach by control of the ring of muscle—the pylorus or gatekeeper—between the stomach and small intestine. Experiments which supported the theory were performed and published. During the decades which have passed since the original observations (on the rate of discharge of different foodstuffs) were reported and the experiments concerned with the theory were described, the suggested regulatory role of the pylorus has not infrequently been criticized. Again experiments have been performed, now to support the criticism, but the methods employed have invariably involved interference with the natural relations. As far as I am aware no one has ever repeated exactly the methods which led to the theory that acid governs the opening and closing of the pyloric muscular ring. This instance is cited not as a complaint but as an illustration. Quite possibly the theory is unfit, but the surest way to prove it unfit is by demonstrating that the evidence on which it was based is unreliable.

It is hardly necessary to mention a humble attitude as a qualification of the man of science. Even though it may not be an essential qualification, it is a highly desirable one. How little we know of the immensity and structure of the universe and of the nature of the earth and all who dwell therein! How meager, during the days of his years, can be the contributions of any investigator toward the solution of the endless mysteries! The only reasonable attitude for the seeker after truth is that of true humility.

In listing the traits which have seemed to me important for a career of investigation—curiosity, imaginative insight, critical judgment, thorough honesty, a retentive memory, patience, good health, generosity, and the rest—I have not attempted to weigh their relative values. Anyhow, that would be difficult. A beginner, who seriously plans a life of productive scholarship, should not be disheartened if he thinks his qualifications do not meet requirements. Training and practice may not lead to perfection, but they will surely compensate for early inadequacy.

# CHAPTER IV

# FAVORABLE AND UNFAVORABLE CIRCUMSTANCES

YEARS AGO when the English biological chemist, Gamgee, was visiting the old Harvard Medical School, he found us all crowded into small, dark, ill-adapted laboratory rooms. After listening to our apologies and complaints he eased us by remarking, "I have never noticed that the nature of the cage determined the singing of the bird." The history of science reveals many instances of admirable investigative studies carried on under heavily adverse conditions. If the reader will permit one more reference to Beaumont, I may point out that his experiments in the frontier fort at Prairie du Chien were conducted in an environment where the very words "scholarship" and "research" would not have been comprehended. Having none of the opportunities for conference and sympathetic discussion with fellow workers; having, indeed, no scientific companions, no library, no journals, no chance of consulting experts in any difficulty, and possessing no laboratory equipment except a thermometer and a few vials, he prosecuted researches on the gastric juice and the gastric digestive processes which have never failed to evoke admiration from all who have read his record. And because he respected "the true spirit of inquiry" and "honestly recorded the result of each experiment exactly as it occurred," his labors, despite the privations he suffered, were fruitful and had influence far beyond the boundaries of his own country, in France, Germany, and Russia.

Fortunately, with the gradual recognition that scientific research yields rich values for the satisfaction of human wishes—

comforts, conveniences, and dramatic conquests of disease—conditions for the experimenting investigator have been vastly improved. Nevertheless, advantageous circumstances are sometimes neglected and disadvantageous circumstances carelessly tolerated; either may affect the advancement of science. They are, therefore, worthy of consideration.

First among favorable conditions I would emphasize freedom of action. As Grundling remarked in an address at the University of Halle, more than two hundred years ago, only liberty allows science to bloom and minds to put forth their full strength. Unless an investigator asks no favors and renders none, unless he is unrestrained by intimation that he act as a special pleader, unless he is released from any demand that his explorations be confined within certain limits lest he injure cherished doctrines and customs, he is sure to lack the inspiration and the zest which spring from independence in pioneering research. The common tradition of academic freedom, at least in the natural sciences, which has been preserved in non-sectarian universities in most civilized countries, has as a rule guaranteed an unfettered mind. In the past, ancient superstitions, doctrinal dogmas, and political ideologies have thwarted truth seekers and even made martyrs of them. Galileo, astronomer, was brought before the Inquisition and condemned; Priestley, a discoverer of oxygen, was attacked by a mob of Tories who sacked his house, destroyed his material possessions, and annihilated the labor of years—and though he and his family escaped, he found security only by emigrating to this country (in 1794); and Lavoisier, French chemist, warmly devoted to the public welfare, was guillotined by blind and cruel revolutionists who had "no need of scholars." In quite recent times, many productive investigators of highest eminence have been forced, for "racial" reasons, to flee from their laboratories and seek refuge in foreign lands. Full liberty of learning, the most potent condition for giving to mankind control of the powers of nature, is not yet assured.

Another highly favorable influence is a feeling of security.

Successful research often requires a continuous and long-lasting program. If such a program is to be rudely interrupted by political changes, and especially if it becomes dependent on political preferment, the research worker, beset by a confusion of mixed motives, cannot give undivided attention to his main purpose. Then, interest in science alone is likely to fade away. In some parts of the world there still are large areas of political turmoil in which the career of the investigator is hazardous or nearly impossible because of the pernicious influence of political adventurers and their personal coteries. Governments under which such conditions prevail are parasitic; though they benefit from the new knowledge gained in other and freer lands, they interfere with the achieving of new knowledge by their own citizens.

Since research is always a pushing forward of exploration from known into unknown regions, the explorer can advance effectively only when he is well acquainted with the background from which he starts. Access to pertinent literature is therefore an important element in the conduct of research. In the larger centers of scholarly activity there are libraries in which complete sets of scientific periodicals, as well as monographs on special subjects, are available. Occasionally I have utilized one of the great advantages which medical investigators in the United States can enjoy—that of obtaining through a local library the temporary loan of books from the priceless collection in the Surgeon General's Library in Washington.

Productiveness is favored, too, by absence of pressure to produce definite results promptly or within a given time. If we knew where and when we could find what we seek, research would not be difficult. *Time* is required for reading and for ruminating and waiting for new ideas, and then for contriving experimental tests and giving them critical application. Michael Foster, the English physiologist, once remarked that "leisure is the mother of discovery." Furthermore, time may be required because unanticipated difficulties are often encountered. As venturers into unknown territory investigators cut their own trails; in doing so they must occasionally stop to find their bearings. The methods of investigative progress are as remote as possible from the methods of machine production. To the eager and expert experimenter any hint of censure or punishment for failure to bring forth results within a given period is almost certain to be harmful. Under such treatment he is likely to be filled with anxiety instead of with fertile thoughts, ardor for the enterprise, and ingenious plans for bringing it to success.

Men of science derive stimulation from gathering together and comparing and discussing their experiences. This is an opportunity which may be made profitable within the confines of a single laboratory. On a larger scale it is experienced at meetings of scientific societies. In the United States, the Federation of American Societies for Experimental Biology, the Association of American Physicians, and the immense American Medical Association hold annual sessions at which the latest steps in progress are described. The accelerated progress of science today has significantly coincided with the establishment of national and international associations which provide opportunities for the members to congregate and to report and debate their recent discoveries. Simultaneously students have migrated freely to foreign lands to benefit from contact with inspiring leaders. These students have returned to their home countries and in many instances they have established centers for the further stimulation of scientific workers and for the promotion of investigative enterprises.

International societies and associations and the migration of students from one country to another illustrate disregard for the barriers of prejudice and exclusive nationalism in scientific thinking. Almost any subject I might select as an example would reveal that contributions to it had been made by scientists in many countries and of different races. A central interest of the Harvard Physiological Laboratory in the 1930's was the work already referred to on the chemical agents which are set free at nerve terminals when the nerves become active and which exert immediate influence on the end organs—muscles and glands. Researches pertinent to this interest were carried on during that decade in Hungary, Austria, Belgium, England and Canada, in Mexico, the Soviet Union, Switzerland, and the United States. Investigators in these countries all published openly their methods and results; all mutually profited by the unrestricted exchange of ideas. There could be no artificial barriers because the world-wide uniformity of scientific phenomena renders such barriers absurd. In a very real sense all who contribute in various lands to the advancement of science in any particular field are collaborators.

The lives and achievements of scientists demonstrate how utterly fantastic is the notion of so-called "nationalistic" science! Nothing could be more erroneous than the declaration of Rust, minister of education, in dedicating the Physical Institute at the University of Heidelberg during Hitler's regime: "It is, then, very superficial to speak of science as being a common property of mankind, equally accessible to all peoples and classes and offering them all an equal field of work. The problems of science do not present themselves in the same way to all men. The Negro or the Jew will view the same world in a different way from the German investigator."

Involvement of a nation in war imposes on men of science obligations which are likely to interfere greatly with their chosen programs of research. Always there is eagerness to be useful when fellow citizens are shedding their blood for the welfare of all. Sometimes current investigations can be given a slightly different direction and thereby be related to the war effort. In other circumstances, however, the interests of the investigator are so remote from practical usefulness in military and naval activities that satisfying the desire to be serviceable involves a sharp break. Such was the case in my experience in 1917 when I left studies of the adrenal glands and undertook studies of wound shock.

Investigators who employ living animals for experimental purposes not only confront more complex problems than do the physicists and the chemists but they also confront a hostile group of zealous opponents. These are the fighting antivivisectionists—of whom I shall have more to say later—the success of whose efforts would interfere with the activities of the investigators and might even abolish the means through which their experimental work can arrive at its beneficent consequences. The word "vivisection" is unfortunate because it has various meanings which are not clearly distinguished. To the antivivisectionists the word too frequently signifies the cutting or dissection of sentient living animals, bound or otherwise restrained and without anesthesia subjected to the full torture of extensive operations. The repeated tales of assumed cruelty, the unexplained illustrations of instruments used in laboratory procedures, and the imaginary pictures of sufferings the animals are supposed to endure at the hands of experimenters indicate the hideous significance attached by the zealots to the word "vivisection."

To the medical investigator, on the contrary, the word has a quite different significance. It means, to be sure, operations on living animals but it does not imply attendant pain, any more than does an operation on a living man by a surgeon. And if an animal is anesthetized, then operated upon, and is killed without recovery from anesthesia, clearly the procedure has not involved any pain whatever. The operation would not have been different in effect, so far as the experience of the animal is concerned, if it had first been killed and later dissected. There is abundant evidence that in almost all physiological experiments the observations on living processes are made in precisely this way, i.e., while the animals are on the way to painless death by anesthesia. In medical investigations substances are injected and sometimes diseases are produced; and in surgical research it is occasionally necessary, after a painless operation, to keep the animals alive in order to observe the effects of the procedure. In these instances of inoculation and aseptic operation, the animals may feel ill, as they would with a distemper. The pain of inoculation is trifling; and in the vast majority of operations even on human beings the aseptic healing of wounds, as I can testify from personal experience, causes no considerable discomfort after full recovery from the anesthetic. Were lower animals as sensitive as man, therefore, the pain would not be great, and there are good indications that they are not as sensitive. The sight of an animal contentedly munching its food a short time after an operation is commonplace in laboratory experience. The total amount of pain resulting from animal experimentation is in all antivivisection literature grossly exaggerated.

Yet the testimony that the immense majority of operations in experimental medicine are attended by little or no suffering is everywhere opposed by the antivivisectionists in their writings. Some of the reports they cite are based on experiments performed more than a century ago, before the discovery of anesthesia; some are frankly of the class of experiments involving slight pain and discomfort; some are clear instances of misrepresentation by persons too unfamiliar with bodily functions and the effects of anesthetic agents to understand ordinary biological description. Many decades since, my teacher of physiology, Dr. H. P. Bowditch, in testing whether a nerve could be fatigued, cut the nerve while the animal was completely under the effects of ether and then stimulated the isolated end. Commenting on this experiment, a representative of the New England Antivivisection Society declared, "It will be readily seen, even by the casual reader, that it involves an amount of agony beyond which science is unable to go and which, to approximate, is impossible except by a person who has devoted long years to the study of nerves." Despite clear explanation that not even trivial pain could be inflicted by stimulating a piece of nerve quite separated from the brain, the society continued for nearly a human generation to broadcast this ancient slander.

More recent studies carried on by me or under my direction

have not escaped denunciation by the antivivisectionists. An operative procedure was performed on cats under scrupulously considerate surgical precautions, in order to avoid both pain and infection, and aftercare was provided which included warmth and a comfortable resting place. Within half a day the animals were up and moving about and took their food as usual the next morning; thereafter they wandered about the laboratory, rubbing their sides against table legs or coming to be petted, and exhibited no signs of discomfort. Yet in an antivivisection periodical they were described as "wretched animals," which had undergone a "frightful operation" and were subjected to "exquisitely contrived torture," suffering "agonies not to be described." Such perverse charges made by persons who did not see what they described are fair illustrations of the sort of criticism to which medical investigators may be subjected. I was once informed: "Such men as you ought to be tarred and feathered and I would like to help do it, too."

While his conscience is quite clear, the "vivisector" is not likely to enjoy being reviled and hearing all manner of evil said against him falsely. Still more unfavorable to his work, however, is the continuous agitation for passage of hostile laws that would restrict freedom of medical research. Commonly, every winter when legislatures meet, there are introduced, now in one state now in another, bills directed toward that dangerous purpose. These efforts, unfortunately, must be met by some of the "vivisectors" themselves. They act for the public to protect from ruthless interference a method of investigation which has done more for mankind, by bringing release from devastating diseases and from premature death, than any other human endeavor. To protect it, however, takes valuable time.

The possibilities of research by simple means have largely disappeared. Expensive apparatus, great amounts of expendable material, and proper assistance—secretarial and technical—are essential in modern research. What generous financial support does for an investigator is to increase and accelerate his output. If he has ample money to aid him he is not compelled to spend time in a shop making necessary apparatus, but can order it made by skillful machinists; he is not required to undertake the labor of rearing and attending to animals for his studies, but can buy the animals from reliable dealers or hire someone to breed them and give them proper care; he need not make charts, graphs, and tables, or prepare tracings and records for publication, but can employ a draftsman to attend to these matters. Just in so far as an investigator is freed from distracting attention to a variety of minor tasks which, though essential, are better performed by expert technicians in the several fields, is he enabled to devote himself to his own special functions—keeping in touch with the moving frontier of knowledge, the newest literature, the latest discoveries; estimating the significance of fresh achievements in other places as related to his own current studies; and, by conferences with his fellow workers and by personal engagement in experiments, participating in the advances into new territory.

A seasoned investigator has many more pregnant ideas than he alone can work upon. His service to society, therefore, can be enhanced by increasing the number of his collaborators. For this reason the establishment of fellowships and research assistantships at his disposal is thoroughly justifiable. When such positions are occupied by intelligent and well-trained young devotees of science they augment the productivity of a leader in research both by adding to his "hands" and by helping to evolve new ideas, methods, and theories in the natural give-and-take of collaboration.

There is some danger in being responsible for a large group of assistants, especially if any of them are inadequately trained and if the director of research is harassed by numerous demands on his attention, not infrequently to affairs outside his laboratory. Data may be reported to him which he has not had time to see acquired and which, although they may involve a systematic oversight, seem to him and to his inexpert subordinate quite reliable. I have known of a grave error being published that resulted from just such circumstances.

Sometimes special, expensive apparatus is needed for the conduct of an investigation. Occasionally travel must be undertaken to reach a region unique for the study of animals in their natural habitat or to obtain rare specimens. One of my former colleagues, Homer W. Smith, who became interested in the evolution of body fluids, had to go to the Nile Valley to get the lung fish, a highly significant intermediate form between water and land inhabitants. Sometimes travel is desirable in order to consult collections of unpublished data or to learn novel methods or to compare uses of the same methods by different investigators. There are occasions when investigators, working on similar problems in different parts of the country, may receive inspiring stimulation by being brought together in conference. Furthermore, proper publication of results may demand costly plates or tables, which journals cannot afford. Indeed, not uncommonly the facilities for appropriate publication of an article are inadequate because of lack of financial assistance. Experience has shown that for all these purposes the spending of money is defensible—defensible in the only way recognized by men of science—because it results in the advancement and spread of knowledge.

Probably a research fund can be employed more economically, certainly it can be employed more efficiently, if the user of the fund knows that he can count on uninterrupted support. When a well-tested and trustworthy investigator is fairly definitely assured that he may expect continuance of financial aid for his researches, he can plan ahead; he can enter on projects which may require years for their completion and often prove to be the most important; and he is freed from worries about the future of his work, worries which may interfere seriously with single-minded devotion to his scientific program.

Whether financial support for scientific research should be sought from private sources and benevolent foundations or from governmental subvention is subject to debate. It certainly seems reasonable that the government should support research generously with the expectation that valuable results would be obtained, that the citizenry would be enriched, and the public welfare promoted. The practical application of such a plan, however, should be safeguarded against possible abuses. A large government fund available for distribution is sure to be the object of political pressure. Administrators of the fund should be sufficiently expert and influential to resist it. Also they should represent different aspects of science so that they are able to evaluate all manner of proposals for investigative under-takings. And they should be strict judges, for inevitably there would be numerous appeals of a highly dubious character and borderline proposals between proper research and projects pri-marily advantageous to individuals or institutions, which would have to be carefully discriminated. Any agency set up to administer a fund assigned by the government for grants-in-aid should, of course, be scrupulously fair in its decisions, act-ing in complete disregard of partisan, social, or racial consid-erations.

Governmental support of scientific studies might bring about a minimizing and possibly at last the disappearance of the financial help hitherto generously bestowed on universities and research institutes by the administrators of the large benevo-lent foundations. When I was Harvard exchange professor for the French universities in 1930, a well-known investigator com-plained to me of the meager funds which came from the gov-ernment to finance research in his laboratory. I pointed out to him that his university was situated in a rich city and sug-gested that an appeal might be made to wealthy men for sup-port of his scientific work. With a shrug of his shoulders he informed me that everybody counted on the central govern-ment to give that support. Indeed, the French felt as little in-clined to contribute private money to improve conditions in the universities as we might feel if asked for money to improve conditions in our post offices.

Lest there be oscillations of interest or of ability on the part of the government in supporting scientific enterprises, the hope may be entertained that by good fortune foundations, which in the past have favored such enterprises, will continue to exist and to exercise a beneficent influence. By assigning proper credit to aid received from the foundations a memorial is preserved of those in whose name they were established. Often this is the recognition the founder desired.

When an investigator carries on his experiments in a university or a research institute, the atmosphere maintained by the officials of the organization may be helpful or otherwise. If the administrative officials are sympathetic, if they do all they can to render the circumstances as favorable as possible to productive work in the laboratories, all may go well. On the other hand indifference, lack of interest, carping criticisms, and a pinching financial policy can be deeply discouraging. Blessed is the scientist who serves under considerate and understanding administrators.

An investigator who is also a teacher in a college or a university can enjoy the opportunities offered by the long summer vacation. If he happens to be eagerly on the trail of a promising idea, he can spend this time in untrammeled experimenting. Or he can use it in getting a thorough acquaintance with a new field of research and in preparing for new undertakings. Again, it offers freedom for writing articles on observations recently completed or for a survey of a group of related studies that are ready for general interpretation. Or, if there is need for recreation and diversion, the free time may be spent for those purposes. Absence from the laboratory may yield profits that are only realized later for, during the fallow months, illuminating suggestions may occur which lead to fresh endeavors.

The question pertinently arises whether highly advantageous conditions for the prosecution of research may not in the end prove to be unfavorable. There are, admittedly, many instances of deterioration of enterprise in the presence of easy circumstances. Will not liberty of inquiry, security of tenure, absence of pressure to produce frequently, substantial support from assistants, and a generous supply of funds—will not these and other favorable circumstances result in subsidence into a life of ease and indolence? Rarely, there are individuals whose ardor for investigation has cooled, who succumb to the opportunity to waste time in idleness. I do not believe, however, that personal hardships and limiting privations are required to render investigators productive. The real devotee of research is driven by an impelling desire to learn, to satisfy his burning curiosity, to know whether his surmise is true or not. Look into an active, well-financed laboratory when a group of experimenters are at work and you will find that enthusiasm for advancing knowledge is mutually stimulating. Even if a member of the group should be inclining to slackness, he would be stirred to action by a spirit of emulation and by a wish to preserve his good repute. Furthermore, a wide survey of scientific progress reveals that as decades have passed, conditions for investigation have become more and more favorable for those engaged in it. Concomitant with that change there has been no indication that seekers for new facts have become remiss and slothful; indeed, the advancement of science has been marvelously accelerated as the conditions have improved.

# CHAPTER V

# THE ROLE OF HUNCHES

How DO investigators obtain insight into ways of possible progress toward acquiring new knowledge? Do they sit down and think intensively about the existing status and what the next move shall be or do they count upon revelation for hints and clairvoyance? Evidence indicates that reliance has been placed on both methods.

From the years of my youth the unearned assistance of sudden and unpredicted insight has been common. While a student in high school I was occasionally puzzled by "originals" in algebra, the solution of which was not at all clear when I went to sleep at night. As I awoke in the morning the proper procedures were immediately evident and the answers were quickly obtained. On an occasion I was handed a complicated toy which was out of order and would not operate. I examined the mechanism carefully but did not see how the defect might be corrected. I resorted to sleep for a solution of the problem. At daybreak the corrective manipulation appeared thoroughly understandable, and I promptly set the contraption going.

As a matter of routine I have long trusted unconscious processes to serve me—for example, when I have had to prepare a public address. I would gather points for the address and write them down in a rough outline. Within the next few nights I would have sudden spells of awakening, with an onrush of illustrative instances, pertinent phrases, and fresh ideas related to those already listed. Paper and pencil at hand permitted the capture of these fleeting thoughts before they faded into oblivion. The process has been so common and so reliable for me that I have supposed that it was at the service of everyone. But evidence indicates that it is not.

An illuminating inquiry into the nature of the flash of ideas and the extent of its occurrence among scientific men was reported by Platt and Baker [1] in 1931. They called the phenomenon a "hunch," a word meaning originally a push or sudden thrust. In ordinary experience it means the quick gleam of a suggestion that flares unexpectedly as the answer to a difficult question or as the explanation of a puzzle. They defined the scientific hunch as "a unifying or clarifying idea which springs into consciousness as a solution to a problem in which we are intensely interested."

In their inquiry into the appearance of hunches among chemists they received answers from 232 correspondents. Assistance from a scientific revelation or a hunch in the solution of an important problem was reported by 33 per cent; 50 per cent reported that they had such assistance occasionally; and only 17 per cent, never. Professor W. D. Bancroft, the Cornell University chemist, tells of talking to four fellow chemists regarding aid from hunches and finding that to three of them the experience was commonplace. The fourth did not understand what was meant by the reference and testified that he had never had the feeling of an inspiration, had never had an idea come to him unexpectedly from some strange "outside" realm. He had worked consciously for all his results and what was described by the others meant nothing to him.

In typical cases a hunch appears after long study and springs into consciousness at a time when the investigator is not working on his problem. It arises from a wide knowledge of facts, but it is essentially a leap of the imagination, for it reaches forth into the range of possibilities. It results from a spontaneous process of creative thought. Noteworthy in the statistics given by Platt and Baker is the evidence that having hunches was not unknown to 83 per cent of the chemists who replied to

[1] W. Platt and R. A. Baker, "The Relation of the Scientific 'Hunch' to Research," *Journal of Chemical Education,* VIII (1931), 1969-2002.

the questionnaire. This high percentage raises the query as to whether the advantage of receiving sudden and unexpected insight might not be cultivated and thus possessed by all.

According to my experience a period of wakefulness at night has often been the most profitable time in the twenty-four hours. This is the only credit I know that can be awarded to insomnia. As an example of an idea which came to me in one such illuminating moment, I will describe a device that was used in the laboratory to obtain an automatically written record of the clotting of blood. It consisted of a very light lever with the long arm ending in a writing point. The long arm was not quite counterweighted by a fixed load on the short arm, but when in addition a small wire was hung on the end of the short arm it slightly overbalanced the other side. The wire was so arranged that it dipped into a small glass tube containing a few drops of blood freshly taken from the running stream in an artery. A check on the long arm prevented the heavier short arm from falling. When the check was lifted, however, the short arm fell and the wire descended into the blood as the writing point rose and wrote a record. This showed that the blood had not clotted. The check was then restored; a minute later it was again lifted and again a record was written. The process was repeated thus at regular intervals. As soon as the blood clotted it supported the light wire and, now, when the check was raised, the heavier long arm did not rise and the fact that the blood had turned to a jelly was registered on the recording surface. All this was presented to me as a complete mechanism in a brief period of insight when I awoke in the night.

Another example I may cite was the interpretation of the significance of bodily changes which occur in great emotional excitement, such as fear and rage. These changes—the more rapid pulse, the deeper breathing, the increase of sugar in the blood, the secretion from the adrenal glands—were very diverse and seemed unrelated. Then, one wakeful night, after a considerable collection of these changes had been disclosed, the idea flashed through my mind that they could be nicely integrated if conceived as bodily preparations for supreme effort in flight or in fighting. Further investigation added to the collection and confirmed the general scheme suggested by the hunch.

A highly interesting instance of the appearance of a hunch with important consequences has been told by Otto Loewi, formerly professor of pharmacology at the University of Graz. The incident is related to the first demonstration of a chemical agent liberated at the end of nerves and, as already mentioned, acting as an intermediary between the impulses which sweep along a nerve and the structures they control. Many years ago T. R. Elliott, while a student at Cambridge, England, had suggested that the reason why adrenaline, when injected into the body or applied to an absorbing surface, mimics the action of sympathetic nerves, might be because these special nerves, when active, discharge adrenaline at their terminals. Thus there would be no essential difference between the effects of adrenaline delivered by the streaming blood and adrenaline serving as a chemical deputy for the arriving impulses. Later, H. H. Dale had proved that the substance, acetylcholine, could mimic the action of such nerves as the vagus, which can cause among other effects a slower beating of the heart. There was no proof, however, that in any condition nerves actually produce their effects by means of a chemical mediator. The crucial problem was that of demonstrating whether the idea was correct or not.

One night, after falling asleep over a trifling novel, Dr. Loewi awoke possessed by a brilliant idea. He reached to the table beside his bed, picked up a piece of paper and a pencil, and jotted down a few notes. On awakening next morning he was aware of having had an inspiration in the night and he turned to the paper for a reminder. To his consternation he could not make anything of the scrawl he found on it. He went to his laboratory, hoping that sense would come to what he had written if he were surrounded by familiar apparatus. In spite of frequently withdrawing the paper from his pocket and studying it earnestly, he gained no insight. At the end of the day, still filled with the belief that he had had a very precious revelation the night before, he went to sleep. To his great joy he again awoke in the darkness with the same flash of insight which had inspired him the night before. This time he carefully recorded it before going to sleep again. The next day he went to his laboratory and in one of the neatest, simplest and most definite experiments in the history of biology brought proof of the chemical mediation of nerve impulses. He prepared two frog hearts which were kept beating by means of a salt solution. He stimulated the vagus nerve of one of the hearts, thus causing it to stop beating. He then removed the salt solution from this heart and applied it to the other one. To his great satisfaction the solution had the same effect on the second heart as vagus stimulation had had on the first one: the pulsating muscle was brought to a standstill. This was the beginning of a host of investigations in many countries throughout the world on chemical intermediation, not only between nerves and the muscles and the glands they affect but also between nervous elements themselves.

In the lives of scientists there are numerous instances of the value of hunches. Helmholtz, the great German physicist and physiologist, when near the end of his life, told of the way in which the most important of his ideas had occurred to him. After investigating a problem "in all directions," he testified, "happy ideas come unexpectedly without effort like an inspiration. So far as I am concerned, they have never come to me when my mind was fatigued or when I was at my working table." Rest was necessary for the appearance of the original ideas and they occurred as a rule in the morning after a night's sleep.

For years during which Darwin was accumulating great numbers of facts he saw no general meaning in them, but felt that they had some great significance which he had not yet perceived. Then, suddenly, the flash of vision came. In his brief autobiography he writes, "I can remember the very spot in the road, whilst in my carriage, when to my joy, the solution occurred to me." Thereafter, with vast toil in the arrangement of facts and in careful exposition, he framed his statement of the theory of biological evolution.

The personal testimony of investigators who have had hunches emphasizes the sudden and startling character of the experience. A few quotations taken from Platt and Baker are illustrative:

"At three o'clock in the morning I awakened with an entirely new process clearly before my mind's eye."

"I came to the plant one Sunday morning about nine o'clock when no one was around. Suddenly it dawned on me that one of the variables was more important than all the others together."

"Sunday in church the correct principles came like a flash as the preacher was announcing the text."

"Freeing my mind of all thoughts of the problem I walked briskly down Tremont Street, when suddenly at a definite spot which I could locate today—as if from the clear sky above me—an idea popped into my head as emphatically as if a voice had shouted it."

"I decided to abandon the work and all thoughts relative to it and then, on the following day, when occupied in work of an entirely different type, an idea came to my mind as suddenly as a flash of lightning and it was the solution. . . . Like other 'hunches' I have experienced in my research work, the utter simplicity made me wonder *why* I hadn't thought of it before."

"The idea came with such a shock that I remember the exact position quite clearly."

"Then the explanation, essentially complete, sprang into my head."

"Instantly the 'hunch' flashed in and said, 'This is the way to produce what you have spent long months of work on.' "

"One day, while sitting at my desk, doing nothing, and thinking about other matters, a thought flashed through my mind. I immediately left the office; went out into the plant by myself; made a few tests, and solved the difficulty."

The foregoing quotations emphasize how surprising and how thoroughly unexpected the fruitful hunch can be.

There has been much discussion of what lies back of the experience of having hunches. They have been ascribed to the operations of the "subconscious mind." This expression seems to me to be a confusion of terms, for it involves the concept that a mind exists of which we are not conscious. I am aware that in psychology this view has been held. Indeed, one psychologist with whom I discussed the matter declared that wherever nerves co-ordinate the activity of muscles, a mind is present. I told him that the nerve net in the wall of the intestine brings about a contraction of muscles above a stimulated point and a relaxation below it so that a mass within the tract is moved onward. This is co-ordinated action, and I asked him whether he would ascribe a mind to the intestine. His reply was, "Undoubtedly." The attitude thus expressed was extreme. It may be taken, however, as a basis for criticizing the assumption that there is a mind wherever nervous activity goes on, when in fact there is no evidence to support the notion. Numerous highly complex responses which can be evoked from the spinal cord and many nice adjustments made by the part of the brain that manages our normal balance and posture are wholly unconscious. There is no indication whatever that anything which we recognize as a mind is associated with these nervous activities.

To me as a physiologist, mind and consciousness seem to be equivalent, and the evidence appears to be strong that mind or consciousness is associated with a limited but shifting area of integrated activity in the cortex of the brain. The physiologist assumes that, underlying the awareness of events as it shifts from moment to moment, there are correlated processes in the enormously complicated mesh of nervous connections in the thin cortical layer. Such activities could go on, however, in other parts of the cortex and at the time be unrelated to the conscious states. They would be similar in character to the activities associated with consciousness, but would be extraconscious. Our knowledge of the association between mental states and nervous impulses in the brain is still so meager that we often resort to analogy to illustrate our meaning. The operation going on in an industry under the immediate supervision of the director is like the cerebral processes to which we pay attention; but meanwhile in other parts of the industrial plant important work is proceeding which the director at the moment does not see. Thus also with extraconscious processes. By using the term "extraconscious processes" to define unrecognized operations which occur during attention to urgent affairs or during sleep, the notion of a subconscious mind or subconsciousness can be avoided.

The question arises as to what conditions are favorable and what unfavorable for the appearance of hunches. Among the unfavorable conditions are mental and physical fatigue, petty irritations, noise, worry over domestic or financial matters, states of depression, and strong emotions. Other unfavorable conditions include being driven to work under pressure and being interrupted or feeling that there may be interruption at any time, as in the demands of administrative duties.

Among the favorable conditions is a great interest in the problem to be solved, a clear definition of this problem, and an eager desire for its solution. A large store of related information already acquired is another prerequisite. The greater the number of facts which are pertinent to the urgent problem and which can be combined in novel ways for explaining the puzzle it presents, the more likely is the puzzle to be solved. The relative facts should be systematically organized; indeed it is better to have a small number of facts well co-ordinated than a great mass of incongruous data. A sense of well-being and a feeling of freedom are other advantageous circumstances. R. S. Woodworth in his *Psychology* has listed as conditions favoring invention a good physical state, a fresh mind, mastery of the subject, striving for a result, confidence, enterprise, willingness to take a chance, eagerness for action, and readiness to break away from routine. A helpful atmosphere for the appearance of a hunch is produced by discussing the problem with other investigators and by reading articles pertinent to it and also pertinent to methods useful for its solution.

The foregoing considerations reveal that the occurrence of a scientific hunch is closely related to antecedent preparations, and that its value is dependent on subsequent activities directed toward testing its validity. The whole process, including the preparatory and the confirmatory stages, is well illustrated in the discovery by Claude Bernard that the liver stores sugar and, when there is need, sets the sugar free. In a study of the phenomena of nutrition, he noticed the important role played by sugar. In testing the blood for its sugar content at various points after its departure from the intestine, where sugar is absorbed, he found less in the blood of the left side of the heart and in the arteries than in the veins. He drew the erroneous conclusion that the sugar was consumed in the lungs. Then Bernard's interest in the metabolism of sugar in the body led him to examine persons suffering from diabetes, and he was struck by the evidence that the output of sugar in the urine of diabetics is greater than that represented in the food they take in. There sprang into his mind a guiding idea that sugar is *produced* in the organism. This was the hunch which had to be tested. He assayed the sugar concentration at various points in the circulatory system and found that after the blood passed through the liver it was richer in glucose than it had been before entering. The conclusion was justified that the excess was derived from the liver.

In order to avoid criticism, however, Bernard supported this evidence by a confirmatory experiment. He fed a dog exclusively on meat, which would not give rise to glucose in the process of digestion, and found that, with the methods he employed at the time, blood in the portal vein leading away from the intestine to the liver was devoid of sugar while that coming away from the liver contained sugar in abundance. In this case the glucose, according to the evidence then available, was derived entirely from liver stores. Finally, in order to meet the objections and doubts of contemporaries who very seriously questioned the ability of animals to produce glucose, Bernard showed that if a current of water is passed through the blood vessels of the isolated liver the time comes when the perfusing fluid contains no trace of sugar. Now, if the liver is exposed to a temperature approximately that of the body, after a few hours abundance of glucose is found in it. In this record of fundamental experiments, revealing a process which Claude Bernard was first to call an "internal secretion," the conscious preparation for the discovery was associated with an erroneous conclusion, but it led to a deep interest in the origin and fate of sugar in the body. His hunch may be regarded as the consequence of that interest and as the basis for the experiments. He definitely established the proof that the hunch was correct and that sugar is actually produced by processes taking place in the animal organism.

Different criteria for classifying scientists engaged in experimental studies have been suggested. Bancroft has proposed two groups: the guessers and the accumulators. The guessers are men who work with use of theories and hypotheses; the accumulators are mainly collectors of facts—often using, to be sure, ingenious and delicate methods in order to learn new facts. According to Platt and Baker the chemists who reported that their ideas came to them consciously were of the accumulator type. Many of them, indeed, declared that the idea of the hunch was quite distasteful. The replies from other chemists indicated that they were typical guessers. It is probable that an inquiry would show that the guessers are usually the revealers of new directions for future research and that hunches are highly significant in their scientific life. Although accumulators and those who may be designated as "gleaners" may not originate novel enterprises, they perform important functions in filling the gaps which may have been left by the more enterprising and bolder spirits.

Some readers may be surprised by the testimony that important advances in science are commonly the result of sudden revelations—really, unearned grants of insight—instead of being the product of prolonged and assiduous thinking. The hunch is not alone in giving the investigator an inviting opportunity to use his talents. As I shall indicate in the next chapter, he is favored at times by the good fortune of happy accidents. Neither the bounties from insight nor the bounties from chance, however, relieve the investigator from the necessity of hard labor, for the suggestion which is presented from either source still has to pass the rigorous test of critical proving before it can be admitted to the realm of truth.

# CHAPTER VI

# GAINS FROM SERENDIPITY

In 1754 Horace Walpole, in a chatty letter to his friend Horace Mann, proposed adding a new word to our vocabulary, "serendipity." The word looks as if it might be of Latin origin. It is rarely used. It is not found in the abridged dictionaries. When I mentioned serendipity to one of my acquaintances and asked him if he could guess the meaning, he suggested that it probably designated a mental state combining serenity and stupidity —an ingenious guess, but erroneous.

Walpole's proposal was based upon his reading of a fairy tale entitled *The Three Princes of Serendip*. Serendip, I may interject, was the ancient name of Ceylon. "As their highnesses traveled," so Walpole wrote, "they were always making discoveries, by *accident* or *sagacity,* of things which they were not in quest of." When the word is mentioned in dictionaries, therefore, it is said to designate the happy faculty, or luck, of finding unforeseen evidence of one's ideas or, with surprise, coming upon new objects or relations which were not being sought.

Readers who remember Bible stories will recall that Saul, the son of Kish, was sent forth to find his father's asses, which were lost. In the discouragement of his failures to find them he consulted one, Samuel, a seer. And Samuel told him not to set his mind on them for they had been found, but to know that he was chosen to rule over all the tribes of Israel. So it was announced, and the people shouted their approval. Thus modest Saul, who went out to seek lost asses, was rewarded by a kingdom. That is the earliest record of serendipity I am aware of.

Probably the most astounding instance of accidental discovery in either ancient or modern history was the finding of the western hemisphere by Columbus. He sailed away from Spain firm in the faith that by going west he would learn a shorter route to the East Indies; quite unexpectedly he encountered a whole new world. It is noteworthy that he was not aware of the significance of what he had found. Indeed, it has been said that he did not know where, in fact, he was going nor where he was when he arrived nor where he had been after his return, but nevertheless he had had the most unique adventure of all time. He realized that he had had a remarkable experience and, by extending the knowledge of what he had done, he laid a course which others might follow. Such consequences have been common when accident has been favorable to one engaged in a search and the enterprise has proved fruitful.

In the records of scientific investigation this sort of happy use of good fortune has been conspicuous. A good example is afforded by the origin and development of our acquaintance with electrical phenomena. It is reported that some frogs' legs were hanging by a copper wire from an iron balustrade in the Galvani home in Bologna; they were seen to twitch when they were swung by the wind and happened to touch the iron. Whether the twitching was first noted by Luigi Galvani, the anatomist and physiologist, or by Lucia Galvani, his talented wife, is not clear. Certainly that fortuitous occurrence late in the eighteenth century was not neglected, for it started many researches which have preserved the Galvani name in the terms "galvanize" and "galvanism." And it also led to experiments by his contemporary, Volta, on the production of electric currents by contact of two dissimilar metals—and thus to the invention of the electric battery—experiments so fundamentally important that Volta's name is retained in the daily use of the words "volt" and "voltage."

Such were the accidental beginnings of the telegraph and indirectly of the telephone, radiobroadcasting, and the promise of practical television. And such also were the beginnings of our knowledge of animal electricity. We now use it, for example, to indicate the disordered state of the heart, because every cardiac contraction sends forth through our bodies an electrical wave, a wave that has a different shape according to the damage in the heart muscle. Only recently have we begun to employ animal electricity to give us information about conditions in the brain. That marvelous organ composed of many billions of nerve cells can display rhythmic electrical pulsations and, when extremely delicate instruments are applied to the scalp, they can reveal the different types of pulsations in rest and activity and the modification in some states of disease.

Even in the growth of electrical science, serendipity has played important roles. It was by pure chance that the mysterious relation between electricity and magnetism was discovered. At the end of a lecture the Danish physicist, Oersted, happened to bring a wire, which was conducting a strong current, to a position above and parallel to a poised magnetic needle. Previously, and by intent, he had held the wire perpendicularly above the needle but nothing happened; now, however, when the wire was held horizontally over and along the needle's length, he was astonished to note that without any visible connection the needle swung around until it was almost at right angles to its former position. With quick insight he reversed the current in the wire and found that the needle then deviated in just the opposite way. Later, Faraday not only confirmed the report that an electric current in a wire can move a magnet but also demonstrated that a moving magnet can cause a current to appear in a wire. From these trifling and casual happenings has gradually evolved our vast modern electrical industry with its immense generators and its ingenious arrangements for distributing extensively over great areas the power which provides us with many highly prized conveniences—light in dark places, a cool breeze on a summer day, heat for our morning toast, refrigeration for perishable food, sparks in motor cylinders, the automatic management of complex machines, safety at sea, and multitudes of devices helpful in our daily lives. When we consider the prodigious and intricate involvement of electricity in the affairs of mankind throughout the world, Galvani's frogs' legs may be regarded as almost equal in historical importance to the caravels of Columbus.

In the biological sciences serendipity has been quite as consequential as in the physical sciences. Claude Bernard, for example, had the idea that the impulses which pass along nerve fibers set up chemical changes producing heat. In an experiment performed about the middle of the last century he measured the temperature of a rabbit's ear and then severed a nerve which delivers impulses to that structure expecting, in accordance with his theory, that the ear deprived of nerve impulses would be cooler than its mate on the other side. To his great surprise it was considerably warmer! Without at first knowing the import of what he had done, he had disconnected the blood vessels of the ear from the nervous influences that normally hold them moderately contracted; thereupon the warm blood from internal organs was flushed through the expanded vessels in a faster flow and the ear temperature rose. Thus by accident appeared the first intimation that the passage of blood into different parts of the body is under the government of nerves— one of the most significant advances in our knowledge of the circulation since Harvey's proof, early in the seventeenth century, that the blood does indeed circulate in the vessels.

Another striking instance of accidental discovery has been described by the French physiologist, Charles Richet, a Nobel laureate. It was concerned with a peculiar sensitiveness toward certain substances—such as white of egg, strawberries, ragweed pollen and numerous others—that we now speak of as *anaphylaxis* or *allergy*. This may result from an initial exposure to the substance which later becomes poisonous to the victim. The phenomenon had been noticed incidentally before Richet's studies, but because it did not receive attention its characteristics were virtually unknown. In his charming little book *Le Savant*, he has told the story of how quite unexpectedly he happened upon the curious fact. He was testing an extract of the tentacles of a sea anemone on laboratory animals in order to learn the toxic dose. When animals which had readily survived that dose were given after a lapse of some time a much smaller dose (as little as one-tenth), he was astounded to find that it was promptly fatal. Richet declares that at first he had great difficulty in believing the result could be due to anything *he* had done. Indeed, he testified that it was in spite of himself that he discovered induced sensitization. He would never have dreamt that it was possible.

Pasteur was led by chance to his method of immunization. One day an old and forgotten bacterial culture was being used for inoculating fowls. The fowls became ill but did not die. This happening was illuminative. Possibly by first using cultures that had little virulence and then repeating the injections with cultures of greater virulence, the animals could be made to develop resistance to infection gradually. His surmise proved correct. By this procedure, as readers of his dramatic biography will remember, he was able to immunize sheep against anthrax and human beings against rabies.

It was an accidental observation which ultimately resulted in the discovery of insulin and the restoration of effective living to tens of thousands of sufferers from diabetes. In the late eighties of the last century, von Mering and Minkowski were studying the functions of the pancreas in digestion. While attempting to secure more evidence they removed that organ from a number of dogs. By good luck a laboratory assistant noticed that swarms of flies gathered round the urine of these animals, a fact which he mentioned to the investigators. When the urine was analyzed, it was found to be loaded with sugar. Thus for the first time experimental diabetes was produced, and the earliest glimpse was given into a possible cause of that disease. We now know that small islands of cells in the pancreas produce an internal secretion which exerts control over the use of sugar in the organism. And we know that when these islands are removed or damaged, sugar metabolism is deranged. An extract from the island cells provides the diabetic sufferer with the insulin he needs.

An unforeseen contingency may occasion scientific advances because of the serious problem it presents. A striking instance is afforded in the use of polished rice. There was no reason to anticipate that the polishing of rice would be harmful to those who depended upon it as a food. Yet removal of the covering from the kernels produced in myriads of victims the disease, beriberi, resulting in immeasurable sorrow and distress. As has been pointed out, however, the study of beriberi, thus unwittingly induced, disclosed not only the cause of that disorder but also started explorations in the whole realm of deficiency diseases and thus led to the discovery of some of the most intimate secrets of cellular processes.

A recent instance of serendipity was the finding of vitamin K, lack of which deprives the blood of an essential element for its coagulation. The Danish investigator, Dam, and his collaborators were working on chemical changes in a certain fatty substance in chicks. They noted that the animals on a special restricted diet often suffered from extensive internal hemorrhages. When the diet was changed to seeds and salts, the bleeding failed to occur. By critical tests the abnormal condition was proved to be due not to lack of any previously known vitamin but to lack of a specific agent contained in the liver fat of swine as well as in certain vegetables and in many cereals. This agent, vitamin K, has proved to be important in surgery. For example, patients afflicted with jaundice, owing to an obstruction in the bile duct, can be relieved by operation; unfortunately in jaundice, however, blood clots very slowly; an operation, therefore, may be attended by disastrous bleeding. This danger can now be readily obviated by feeding vitamin K (with bile salts), for it restores to an effective concentration the deficient element of the clotting process, a benefaction which has come to human beings from a chance observation on chicks.

In the life of an investigator whose researches range extensively, advantages from happy chance are almost certain to be encountered. During nearly five decades of scientific experimenting instances of serendipity have several times been my good fortune. Two experiences I mention elsewhere, but not in relation to serendipity. One was stoppage of the movements of the stomach and intestines in times of anxiety. The other was the strange faster beating of the heart, after all its governing nerves were severed, if the animal became excited or if sympathetic fibers were stimulated in some remote region of the body. This effect, due to an agent carried to the heart by the circulating blood, led to the discovery of *sympathin*. Both phenomena were quite unexpected. Proof that the stoppage of digestive movements was due to emotion was the beginning of many years of research on the influence of fear and rage on bodily functions. And the unraveling of the mystery of sympathin led ultimately to prolonged studies on the chemical mediator that serves to transmit influences from nerve endings to the organs they control.

There are many other examples of serendipity which I might detail; among them Nobel's invention of dynamite, Perkin's stumbling upon the coal-tar dyes, and Pasteur's finding that a vegetable mold causes the watery solution in which it is nurtured to change the direction of the light rays as they pass through. Dynamite placed gigantic powers in the hands of man; the coal-tar dyes have fundamentally affected such varied activities as warfare, textile industries, and medical diagnosis; and Pasteur's casual observation has developed into an immense range of chemical theory and research.

Three legends of accidental leads to fresh insight serve to introduce the next point, which is quite as important as serendipity itself. I refer to the presence of a prepared mind. It is said that the idea of specific gravity came to Archimedes as he noted by chance the buoyancy of his body in water. We have all heard the tale, illustrative even if not authentic, that the concept of a universal law of gravitational force occurred to Isaac Newton when he saw an apple fall from a tree while he lay musing on the grass in an orchard. Of similar import is the story that the possibility of the steam engine suddenly occurred to James Watt when he beheld the periodic lifting of the lid of a tea kettle by the steam pressure within it. Many a man floated in water before Archimedes; apples fell from trees as long ago as the Garden of Eden (exact date uncertain!); and the outrush of steam against resistance could have been noted at any time since the discovery of fire and its use under a covered pot of water. In all three cases it was eons before the significance of these events was perceived. Obviously a chance discovery involves both the phenomenon to be observed and the appreciative, intelligent observer.

I may now add to these legends and their illustrative significance the history of that marvelously powerful enemy of infection, penicillin. In 1929 the English bacteriologist, Alexander Fleming, reported noticing that a culture of pus-producing bacteria underwent dissolution in the neighborhood of a mold which accidentally contaminated it. This was the pregnant hint. A careless worker might have thrown the culture away because of the contamination. Instead, Fleming let the mold grow in broth and thus learned that there passed into the broth from the mold a substance which was highly efficacious in stopping the growth of a wide range of disease-producing germs and destroying them. Furthermore he learned that, when injected, this substance was not itself harmful to animals. The mold, a variety of Penicillium, suggested the name "penicillin." The long struggle of Howard Florey and his associates at Oxford in purifying and standardizing this highly potent agent and in proving its value in human cases cannot be recounted here. The record, however, reports one of the most striking instances of immense value that can result from a combination of chance and an alert intelligence; and shows how a brilliant discovery is made practical by hard labor.

Long ago Pasteur recognized that when accident favors an investigator it must be met by sharp insight, for he uttered the wise and discerning dictum, *"Dans les champs de l'observation, le hasard ne favorise que les esprits préparés."* Even before Pasteur, Joseph Henry, the American physicist, enunciated the same truth when he said, "The seeds of great discoveries are constantly floating around us, but they only take root in minds well prepared to receive them."

In the course of human living no one can tell what new circumstances may arise, nor can one predict the moment of their arrival. Tomorrow opportunities may appear the seizure of which or the neglect of which may have long-lasting and fateful consequences. There is a tide in the affairs of all of us, whether investigators or not, which "taken at its flood leads on to fortune," and not taken, may lead on to failure or misfortune. In other words, the unexpected is frequently happening in our ordinary lives, much as it happens in the realm of exploration and scientific research. Chance throws peculiar conditions in our way and, if we have intelligent and acute vision, we see their importance and use the opportunity chance provides.

If we are to benefit by opportunities for securing fresh insight and for enlarging our experiences in untried directions we must be well equipped with knowledge of the past. Only when we know what has been done by earlier contributors can we judge the present scene. We can then bring to bear, in unanticipated circumstances, the memories of bygone events. A historical reference in a speech or in literature or a name in a poem is enriched with a wider fringe of meaning if we embellish it with associations from our own store of knowledge. "In Xanadu did Kubla Khan a stately pleasure-dome decree" are words which do not demand information in order to appreciate their musical beauty, but if we know the story of Kubla Khan as the poet knew it and are acquainted with Oriental magnificence, the words have an extensive and peculiar significance. Furthermore, when the mind has been abundantly prepared, there is always the favorable possibility of continuing enrichment as we grow older. We bring to the reading of literature or history, to the unpredictable incidents of travel, to the illuminating moments of conversation, and to the varied adventures of the passing years, a substantial basis on which can be gradually developed manifold interests and pleasurable relations with our fellows and our surroundings.

Another implication in Pasteur's dictum that chance favors the prepared mind is the importance of avoiding rigid adherence to fixed ideas. It is quite natural for the unenterprising intelligence to find a comfortable security and serenity in a set of conventional opinions which have been satisfactorily prearranged. The unusual is promptly dismissed because it does not fit into the established plan. To persons who live according to pattern, adventures in ideas are impossible. Actually we dwell in a world which is not settled, not stationary, not finally immobilized. It presents all manner of possibilities of novel and unprecedented combinations and readjustments. Consequently, wisdom counsels keeping our minds open and recipient, hospitable to new views and fresh advances. We err if we dismiss the extraordinary aspects of experience as unworthy of attention; they may be the little beginnings of trails leading to unexplored heights of human progress. In a world organization which is in flux, in an anxious society groping its way possibly to new forms should we close our eyes and refuse attention? The solutions may arrive quite unheralded. Unless we are willing to weigh novel ideas and methods on their merits and to judge them justly, we may not be participants in momentous decisions, but instead may be worried and unhappy bystanders.

Most of my illustrations of serendipity have been drawn from the physical and biological sciences. In political, economic, and social affairs, likewise, important and pressing questions are calling for responses. A better world for all of us will be ours when these questions are answered. Many new discoveries are needed in order that these questions may be answered. How can we find ways to achieve more perfect justice among men? How can there be a fairer distribution of the abundance agriculture and industry can produce? What conditions can be devised that will promote good health and effective medical care? How can we be freed from the distress caused by great oscillations between financial booms and depressions? What can be done to reduce crime and the number of criminals, to stabilize family life, and to avoid or rectify numerous other maladjustments? Discoveries that will yield deeper insight into modes of resolving these urgent, difficult and apparently baffling social problems are likely to be made by minds characterized by learning and by liberality, ready to take prompt advantage of fortunate events which, amid extremely complex situations, are sure to appear. Quite unforeseen possibilities will unexpectedly spring forth, chances of serendipity which the sagacious can utilize.

# CHAPTER VII

# PASSING ON THE TORCH

IT HAS been said, "He who can, does. He who cannot, teaches." This slur upon an essential profession in civilized society I resent because it displays a harmful ignoring of the many teachers who "can" and "do," not only by diffusing information but also, and more important, by awakening in young persons intellectual enthusiasms. Scientific investigators who are likewise teachers escape the harsh comment on still wider grounds. Like others in the educational profession they are, to be sure, busy in transmitting knowledge and endeavoring to inspire devotion to scholarly pursuits, but in addition they act effectively in carrying on their researches. They have two important functions to perform—discovering new facts and securing and training recruits who will continue productive scholarship when they have gone.

Universities offer the opportunity of combining the two functions of teaching and investigation. In these centers the productive scholar is highly appreciated, both for his discoveries and for the worthy example he sets before young persons in his persistent devotion to the increase of knowledge. Teachers who are investigators, filled with an ardor for discovery and acquainted with ways to nature's hidden secrets, arouse in young men the qualities they themselves possess. In the companionship of such teachers students catch glimpses of a possible approach to regions still unmapped and are stimulated to become likewise eager in the desire for exploration. That is the theory of the presence of investigators in universities; thereon is based the trust in their influence over the youth whom they instruct.

The richness of university life flows from such noble memories as that which inspired the companions of Maxwell in Cambridge, as they recalled, in him, "the eager thirst for truth, the subtle thought, the perfect temper, the unfailing reverence, the singular absence of any taint of the breath of worldliness in any of its thousand forms."

One advantage presented to the investigator by the combination of research and teaching arises from the duty imposed upon him, as a teacher, of reviewing annually much or all of the field he cultivates. During the year, progress has been made through both his own investigations and those of other scientists. The facts he is expounding, therefore, have fresh relations to the new developments, and these relations may not be perceived until the former knowledge is again reconsidered. I have had the experience, and I imagine other investigators likewise have had it, of a new idea flashing suddenly into consciousness in the midst of a lecture, an idea which might not have arisen if I had not just been engaged in a general survey of my subject.

Another advantage of associating teaching with research is the mutually helpful relationship between the teacher and investigator on the one hand, and admirably trained young men on the other. These students usually approach the subject with a quite fresh point of view. If they are properly stimulated to thinking about what they learn, they will suggest problems or ask questions involving problems that are often of interest and importance. I recall the query of a student who asked me whether the long column of blood reaching from the head to the toes does not require an adjusted increasing degree of muscular contraction in the walls of the arteries as the position changes from horizontal to vertical and the weight of the column, therefore, gradually increases toward the lower portions of the body. I do not yet know the answer to that interesting question. In my experience rarely did a year pass without my receiving from students, in conferences or in conversation, valuable suggestions for further study.

It has been claimed that institutes for medical research offer more desirable positions for investigators than do the universities. There are no teaching obligations; the experimenter can give himself wholly to thinking and working on the problem or problems that enthrall him. However, is not the absence of an occasional general review of the subject, a review which forms a background for special studies, likely to lead the worker to become more and more specialized and perhaps too closely and narrowly tied to his particular concern? Certainly that is a danger to be recognized and resisted. The colleagues who work with leaders in research institutes are not novices; they are already disciplined in methods of investigation before they are accepted as co-workers. The eminent men who head departments in the institutes do not perform, therefore, the highly valuable service of bringing new recruits into scientific endeavor. They have to depend upon the leaders of research in universities to provide them with their assistants. In spite of the advantages claimed for research institutes there is some doubt whether they have to their credit more important discoveries than those that have come from university laboratories where, as I have noted, activities are likely to be more diverse.

If university classes are not too large, capable and eager students may be given the opportunity, during the ordinary curriculum, of being introduced into the methods and excitements of scientific investigation. There are eminent investigators who made their initial contribution to science while they were undergraduates, and some highly important facts have been established by novices. Augustus Waller was a first-year student at the University of Paris when he began special studies which led finally to his proving that nerve fibers are parts of nerve cells, undergoing *Wallerian degeneration* when they are separated from the cell nucleus. The renowned physiologist and physicist, Hermann von Helmholtz, had published, before he received his medical degree, a paper on fermentation induced by yeast. As an undergraduate Paul Ehrlich devised methods of staining blood cells and thereby differentiating various kinds of blood diseases. And Paul Langerhans, who discovered the island cells which produce insulin, began his study of the pancreas when he was still a student. In the Harvard Laboratory of Physiology as well as in other laboratories and in other medical schools able undergraduates have been given their primary insight into the ways of discovery. In two schools with which I am especially acquainted the students report each year at a public gathering the results of their investigations. For example, the value of blood plasma as an emergency treatment for severe hemorrhage was first demonstrated by two medical students. Young persons who undertake original studies along with their regular medical work are not likely to be satisfied with an appeal to authority; they have had insight into the conditions of discovery and have established a basis for understanding the progress of science and the inevitable changes it involves.

Contact with the original records of classic research is stimulating to a young person with scholarly aptitudes. Who can read William Harvey's ingenuous account of his difficulties in understanding the shutting and opening of the chambers of the heart—"motions occurring, as it seemed, variously and confusedly together," accomplished in many animals "in the twinkling of an eye, coming and going like a flash of lightning," so that he was almost tempted to think the motions were "only to be comprehended by God"—who can read that testimony without realizing vividly the pioneer's early mystified impression as he encounters something new, difficult and strange? The student resorting to firsthand reports not only learns about the background for the specific inquiry but also about the methods used, the results obtained, the precautions taken to avoid error, the conclusions drawn from the observed facts. And perhaps he may be stirred by the thrill of the discovery itself. The reading of a considerable number of related papers will reveal the gaps in what is known and the differences of testimony that must sometimes be confronted. Thus the student may perceive opportunities for further experimentation which would yield valuable new knowledge. Thus also he learns that his textbook is a selection of facts that the author has regarded as important and is not the whole story and, further, that the summary set forth in a textbook may neglect or smooth out discrepancies.

Students of a scientific subject should be impressed with the importance of referring to demonstrable facts rather than to printed declarations. I hope that those who have been under my instruction have become so accustomed to the query, "What is the evidence?" that they have not forgotten it and never will forget it. Reliance on a textbook inclines a student to refer to the book for justification instead of citing the facts that lie back of his statement. Only by due regard to the facts does he become independent of the author of the book. Furthermore, it is important to learn to discriminate between facts which have been observed and inferences which are drawn from them. Much of the confusion in ordinary thinking and, indeed, a common reason for disputes spring from the failure to recognize this consequential distinction. Considerate men may find that they agree regarding the facts and then may decide to disagree regarding interpretations.

For medical students especially, the idea that knowledge of phenomena is not fixed and static but continuously growing must be repeatedly stressed. Perhaps there is no realm of scientific enterprise in which progress is being more rapidly made than in medicine. Students should learn, therefore, that the routine curriculum of a medical school provides only the beginning of their education. If they are to be useful efficient physicians they must be always alert to learn and apply the discoveries which are constantly being made and which may be of the utmost importance for their patients.

As a rule students of medicine are so deeply impressed by the seriousness of their professional preparation and by the rigorous demands made upon them that they work continuously and conscientiously. Once in a while, however—and I am sure other teachers will agree—there are students who neglect attention to their studies until shortly before examinations and then

begin to work furiously and ply their teachers and their classmates with all manner of questions. I have called such students
"long-distance putters." This designation was suggested to me
by the story of the complacent golfer who teed his ball, looked
away to the next green, and declared confidently, "That's good
for one long drive and a putt." He swung his driver, tore up
a stretch of sod, and managed to move the ball a few feet off
the tee. The caddy then stepped forward, handed him the put-
ter, and suggested, "Now for a hell of a putt."

For many decades I taught large classes. As the years passed,
I found that my gratifying ability to recognize and name former
students on meeting them gradually deteriorated. The recall-
ing of names became especially difficult. The disability has multiple causes—accumulating numbers of graduates, lessening attention to the individuals of a class as outside duties mount,
and probably a diminishing plasticity of the brain as age advances. One way of escaping the distress experienced when an
eager former student approaches and his name does not
promptly flash into memory was demonstrated to me by the
late Gideon Wells of the University of Chicago. At a meeting of the American Medical Association we were walking together along a street in Minneapolis when a bright, enthusiastic
young extrovert came toward us rapidly with outstretched
hand, exclaiming, "I do not suppose you remember me, Dr.
Wells, but I was one of your students!" "I remember your face
perfectly," Wells affably replied, "but I do not remember the
names of men unless they have to take the course twice!" The
student appeared to be pleasantly satisfied with his encounter.

Years of experience have built up within me the conviction
that education can be acquired only by earnest effort on the
part of students. This conviction implies that experience with
laboratory experiments and conferences between the teacher
and small groups of students in which there is free and informal discussion, instead of a one-way quiz, are much to be preferred to an elaborate and prolonged series of lectures. When
I was a medical student in the late nineties it was customary

for us to be subjected to four hours of continuous lecturing, from two until six o'clock five days of every week, mainly on subjects concerned with human beings, their diseases, the means of diagnosing the diseases, and the proper modes of treatment. At that time my roommate was a law student, Harry A. Bigelow, later dean of the Law School at the University of Chicago. I could not help noting the eagerness and zest with which he and his fellow students discussed cases and their implications and comparing this with the dreary and benumbing process we medical students endured as we filled our notebooks. In my senior year in the Medical School I wrote an article which was published in *The Boston Medical and Surgical Journal* under the title, "The Case System of Teaching Systematic Medicine." The idea of using printed clinical records, that I suggested as a basis for discussing diagnosis and proper treatment, was at once favorably received and put to use. Case books on diseases of the nervous system, on general medicine, and on diseases of children soon appeared. Many of the hours which had formerly dragged in mere passive recording in notebooks what the professor recited—often from another notebook!—now sped away in a lively exchange of views among the students themselves and with their instructors. That reform started about 1900. In the four decades since then more and more emphasis has been placed on case teaching, though the printed records of cases have not been so much used in recent years as they were earlier.

I have been haunted by the idea, which may have its proper setting in this chapter, that in the handling of a complicated case *wisdom* is concerned with appropriate *action*. When we are bewildered and go for advice to a man who has the reputation of being wise, we do so, commonly, in order to know what course to take. If this idea is granted, there are some interesting consequences which flow from it. Medical students, for example, are given instruction in what to do in complex circumstances. That instruction is based upon past experience of physicians who have reported their failures and successes in caring for the victims of disease. In brief, students of medicine are taught not only the facts necessary for understanding the phenomena of bodily disorders, they are also taught what to do, i.e., they are taught wisdom. The question arises whether our educational system is not, in general, too largely concerned with imparting facts and too little with teaching how to act usefully in our intricate civilization. Does not the young graduate go forth to take his place in society with quite inadequate training for his functions and duties in his community? Possibly the case method could be employed systematically and profitably to teach commendable behavior to young citizens.

A great fault in the organization of the American university has been the use of productive scholars for administrative services. As bearing on this fault, one of my experiences may be instructive. I was asked to accept the deanship in a western university medical school. When I protested to the president of the university that I was deeply interested in research, he declared with much enthusiasm, "That's just why we want you. You can go on with your researches and the deanship will take care of itself." Unwilling to accept the president's testimony regarding the ease of serving as dean, I went to two of my friends, both productive scholars, who had recently been impressed into deanships. I conversed with them separately; their responses were almost identical. When I asked about the possibility of continuing scholarly work while holding an executive position, each one threw up his hands and declared that it was well-nigh impossible. They explained that important questions repeatedly and frequently arise which have to be decided with due care for the consequences. Time has to be given to imagining what the consequences would be if the decision lay in one direction and what they would be if it lay in other directions. Unless these questions are thoughtfully considered, there is a guilty sense of not having properly performed the duties of the office. And what can one do for productive scholarship in such circumstances? Or if one pays attention to productive scholarship what sort of dean must one be? The conflict between scholarly activity and administrative duties need not arise if persons who are not productive investigators are selected for administrative work.

Time, as I have emphasized elsewhere, is an essential requirement for effective research. An investigator may be given a palace to live in, a perfect laboratory to work in, he may be surrounded by all the conveniences money can provide; but if his time is taken from him he will remain sterile. On the other hand, as the history of science abundantly shows, an investigator may be poverty-stricken, he may be ill-clothed, he may live in a garret and have only meager appliances for his use; but given time he can be productive.

Since the investigator is ordinarily a subordinate in an administrative organization he may have to confer with administrative superiors on matters which may have important consequences for him and his work. Commonly the conferences are oral and unrecorded. Unless care is exercised, misunderstandings may arise. In order to avoid possible later difficulties due to differences of remembrance of events occurring in a conference, it has been my practice immediately afterward to write down my understanding of what was said and to send it to the officer concerned, with the request that he read it carefully and return it with his modifications or with a statement that it is a true report. Thus what was discussed is put down in black and white in the form of a record to which both parties have agreed.

I cannot end this chapter without testifying to the deep pleasure that the teacher enjoys year after year as he sees the influence of his instruction awakening young persons to interest in and devotion to the subject which he teaches. It is as if he were privileged to take to a high eminence a group of eager and earnest companions and to reveal to them in their fresh enthusiasm the wonders of the scene before them. The enthusiasm then oscillates between the teacher and his followers, each one stimulating the other.

# CHAPTER VIII

# FELLOWSHIP IN EXPLORATION

ONE OF the satisfactions the scientific investigator enjoys is learning about other investigators in his own and in foreign lands who are working on problems linked to those with which he himself is concerned. Thus at various times in my experience I have had collaborators in different parts of the United States, in England, France, South America, Algiers, and Japan. This is, admittedly, remote collaboration, but since there is in scientific effort little regard for national boundaries and since there is free interchange of reports of progress through letters and the reprints of published articles, the relations are those of men working together. The happy result is a wealth of acquaintance that may be world-wide. Though this acquaintance may not for many years become personal, yet if a meeting does take place, it is all the more pleasurable because of the background of fellowship established by sharing ideas.

Besides the bonds which develop between an investigator and his contemporaries, there are the connections with those who have labored before him in scientific effort. As he engages in research he learns of earlier pioneers who have advanced to positions from which he is starting. He may regard himself, therefore, as collaborating with workers in the past as well as with workers of today. When he looks back to his predecessors he may quite reasonably come to feel that he belongs to an extensive family of related members, related not by blood but by intimacy of scientific interests. This concept is illustrated by the heritage transmitted from a leader to his disciples. For example, in this sense I am a son of Bowditch, who led me into physiological investigation. Dr. Bowditch in turn was the son of Karl Ludwig, to whose laboratory in Leipzig in the last century he resorted together with other young men from many lands. Through my grandfather Ludwig, I am related to others of his descendants, among them the Italian physiologist Mosso, the English pharmacologist Brinton, and the Russian physiologist Pavlov. In my own place in this sequence of familial relationship I have scattered sons—and some grandsons—young doctors who have engaged in research in the Harvard Physiological Laboratory and then have returned to their native lands, there to continue physiological investigation.

A pleasant consequence of life in a laboratory where men from different countries, often far from one another, are brought together, is the international friendships that are established. Representatives from countries so slightly related as Chile and Hungary found in the scientific atmosphere of the group about me congenial circumstances for mutual admiration and for cordial good fellowship.

It has been interesting to watch the change of attitude of some foreigners as they gradually became acquainted with unconventional American customs. I well recall one brilliant young investigator who for a time after his arrival would knock on my door and when I said, "Come in," would open the door, elaborately close it behind him, turn toward me as I sat some distance away, click his heels together, and before approaching would bow deeply from the waist. I recognized that that was his expression of respect for a professor. It appalled me! At the tea we held late every afternoon in one of the laboratory rooms it was customary for all of us to talk about the day's work, to bandy jokes, and to swap humorous experiences. This young man was astounded by the freedom and informality of the relations between the professors and their collaborators. Not many months passed, however, before he was playing his part in the give-and-take of friendly conversation. And on the day of his departure for home he came without ceremony to speak to me in my office and confessed that, though he was at first somewhat horrified by the American lack of formality in academic relations, he had become convinced that it was an improvement on that to which he had been accustomed. Furthermore, he had entered the United States despising the ways of democracy, but he was leaving with the belief that it was the best way of life.

In receiving a young investigator as a member of the research group one does well to learn first his personal interest. If it can be attached to a general program already underway, two advantages result: he works eagerly from the start because he is satisfying his own curiosity, and the program of the laboratory is at the same time being advanced. If the interest of the applicant is not at all relevant to researches in progress or to previous experiences of members of the staff, and if he cannot be dissuaded from proceeding as he has planned, he should be advised to go to another laboratory where work appropriate to his project is going forward. This may seem both a neglect of opportunity and a harsh judgment. It is based, however, on experience which has shown that as a rule it results in advantage to all concerned. For the newcomer especially it is pertinent. If he remains, with his incongruous technique and ideas, he finds himself associated with a staff too busy with their own researches and academic duties to learn his ways; consequently he has no one to help him when he runs into difficulties or to criticize intelligently either his methods or his results. If he decides to fit his efforts into the general laboratory strategy he can be assured that as soon as he is well started in any investigation he will almost certainly become fascinated by its enticing possibilities.

For young men entering a laboratory to be trained in research, there is definite advantage in a staff including not only the head of the department but also others who are experts and who can themselves direct the discipline of beginners. If these experienced associate members of the staff have interests different from those of the department head, multiple opportunities are offered for satisfying personal inclinations and diverse inquiries. In addition, there is obvious advantage to the young men in broadening and enriching their knowledge of the methods and of the progress in various endeavors, for frequent conversations and conferences assure a helpful sharing of information about what is being done.

In general, physiological research has been conducted in two different directions: one, toward analysis of the functions of isolated organs and tissues in search of a physical or chemical or physico-chemical explanation of the processes they display; the other, toward a synthesis of the functioning of organs and systems of organs as they co-operate in the behavior of the organism as a whole. The British physiologist, J. S. Haldane, wrote rather scornfully of the former method as a mere study of the "scraps and fragments" of the body, ignoring the marvels of bodily organization. It should be recognized, however, that we should know little of the workings of the heart, for example, and the peculiar features of cardiac muscle, if the heart had not been investigated in isolation. In many respects learning about processes in separated parts of the organism was necessary first in order that the integrated actions of the body as a unified congeries of systems could be understood.

I was fortunate in having as associates Alexander Forbes and Hallowell Davis, highly expert investigators often concerned with analytical methods, whereas my attention was directed mainly toward synthetic or integrative physiology, the responses of the total organism. The variety of our endeavors in solving physiological problems was an additional advantage to our young collaborators because it gave them direct demonstration of the virtues of the two research methods.

It may be pertinent at this point to call attention to the different ways in which investigators select the problems they attempt to solve. There are some who flit from one subject to another as fresh excitements develop from promising discoveries in other places. This may be called following the fashions in science. Other investigators march onward step by step, as observations they have made suggest to them other observations that should be made. My experience exemplifies chiefly the latter type of investigative habit. Early observations on mechanical activities of the alimentary tract revealed its remarkable sensitiveness to emotional excitement. Stoppage of these activities in times of excitement led to studies of other bodily changes which are associated with strong emotions and which are induced by impulses delivered by nerves of the sympathetic system. Continuance of the bodily changes for some time after the occasion for the emotional disturbance had disappeared led to an interest in control of the central portion, the medulla, of the adrenal glands. It secretes adrenaline, a substance which, as the reader will recall, can produce the identical effects that are brought about by sympathetic impulses. When I removed the sympathetic system surgically, the animals deprived of it were unable to maintain their usual resistance to disturbances of the stability of the internal conditions of the body; from these results emerged the concept that the sympathetic system acts to maintain stable states in the organism, to preserve *homeostasis.* Also when the system was removed, a chemical substance given off at the ends of sympathetic nerves disappeared; this result opened another field of study concerned with the chemical intermediary between nerves and the organs they affect. The only intrusion into this series of sequential groups of researches was a study of wound shock, for which, as World War I demonstrated, there was urgent need. While an investigator is progressing from one group of interests to another in such a sequence he gradually gains greater ability to satisfy the desires of persons who come to work with him, should they select studies in any of the fields where he himself has labored.

No more important aid can be rendered to a novice in research than to give him such instruction and supervision as will start him, from his first efforts, toward habits of good workmanship. Holding him to high standards at the beginning makes much easier for him the technical aspects of his later activities and also much easier for others the judgment of what he has really done. A general rule which I have insisted on and which, I am pleased to remark, has received much approval from my associates when they have learned its value is that every graphic record of an experiment shall be so perfect that it is fit for publication. When ideal performance is demanded in a company of workers the desire to accomplish it becomes a motive for competitive striving.

The treatment of his collaborators by the head of a laboratory may be put to a real test when the time arrives for publishing papers. Methods which have proved satisfactory in my experience through several decades are as follows. If I have merely suggested the problem to be investigated, indicated the pertinent literature, demonstrated the method to be employed, and from time to time have supervised the work, I have not allowed my own name to appear on the published paper as a joint author. Although the beginner who has carried on research in these circumstances has usually thanked me graciously at the end of his report, that acknowledgment has never been requested. When I have participated in the experimental procedures, my name has appeared as one of the authors. If I have done a major part of the work my name has been placed first, but if my role has been secondary it has not had that prominent position.

The head of a laboratory performs a valuable service in applying to the written reports prepared by his disciples the larger experience in scientific exposition which his years have given him. Novices learn much from seeing the errors they have committed and the corrections that have been made. Prominent among the corrections commonly required in papers of novitiates is the elimination of certain words carelessly used. In a biological system all the elements of which cannot be known, the words "must," "absolutely," "doubtless," and "invariably" should be used not at all or with extreme caution. As I explain elsewhere, the title of a paper should be so precise and detailed as to indicate clearly its content. If this is not done, an important observation may be hidden away and overlooked by persons who later engage in research in the field. Another suggestion I have offered to my collaborators is that, in the summary at the end of an article, the author refer to the illustrations that make clear the points there stated. Thus the reader has not only a résumé of the contents but an immediate designation of the figures confirming the individual statements.

As already noted, an investigation, if successful, commonly reveals not only the facts sought but also other facts which suggest new directions of work. Scope for scientific inquiry, therefore, is interminable. The new disclosures often present a puzzling situation which the young investigator may have difficulty in meeting. Where shall he stop? When shall he regard his investigation as complete? There are instances of men experienced in research who go on and on conducting their investigations without reporting them, because the new disclosures seem so importantly related to the original purpose that they cannot bring themselves to the point of publishing. Since no research can be final, every publication is a progress report. One does well to keep in mind the initial aim in the investigation. If positive results have been obtained substantiating the originating idea, it is wise to record them in a well-recognized periodical and to withhold the description of fresh insights until new evidence concerning their significance has been secured.

There is a difference of practice among scientific men with regard to publishing speculations suggested by their results. Nothing is easier than to let one's imagination spin fancies on the basis of slight evidence. Fancies may or may not later prove true. As a rule it has seemed to me wiser to advise beginners to confine their report to the facts which have been obtained in the course of investigation and to withhold intimated possibilities derived from these facts until there has been further study.

The leader of a group engaged in research should always be generous in the care and treatment of those with whom he is working. This is an attitude they thoroughly appreciate and always remember. Warren P. Lombard, long professor of physiology at the University of Michigan, has told an illuminating story of his experience in Ludwig's laboratory to which, when a young man, he went for training. He told the professor that he was interested in fatigue but knew nothing about how to study it. Ludwig then defined a concrete problem for him, assembled the apparatus, and set him at work. When he encountered difficulties the old teacher helped him. At the end Dr. Lombard wrote an account of the methods he had used and the results he had obtained and submitted it to the professor preliminary to publication. In a short time the paper was returned almost entirely rewritten, with only Lombard's name at the top of it. He took the paper to Ludwig and protested. "You have set the problem for me," he said; "you have shown me how to use the apparatus and solve my troubles; you have rewritten the paper, and your name should appear here with mine." "No," Professor Ludwig replied. "You have done the work and you should have the credit. But," he added, "if you never do anything more, people will think that *I* did it!"

The leader of a research group should not be credited with all the discoveries that emerge from the group's activity. Young collaborators, disciplined in the basic and commonly in the medical sciences, bring to the problems in which they are engaged new ideas and suggestions occurring to them as they progress in their research. Furthermore, the truth of a principle which Josiah Royce, the philosopher, once enunciated is often exemplified. He stated in somewhat ponderous terms that one can always count on "the fecundity of aggregation." Precisely because men are gathered together and talk freely about their problems, fresh thoughts emerge and are elaborated. In any active laboratory where there is a generous spirit these incidental favors are recognized as part of the common endeavor to advance knowledge. In popular judgment, however, the head of the laboratory is all too frequently praised as the source of all the ideas to which not only he but his collaborators as well have applied their skill and intelligence.

There is one final service a leader in research can perform for his disciples. When they take up responsibilities in their own laboratories they may be lacking the books, the periodicals, and the apparatus necessary to go on in extensions of their research training and ideas. One of the tragedies of an intellectual life is to be possessed by eagerness for trying ventures toward discovery and be thwarted by dearth of facilities for doing just that. Often it is possible to send reprints and books, and to use one's knowledge of the situation to secure from the administrators of funds, who desire to make good investments, grants—even small grants—which provide the financial aid needed by a young investigator. Such aid allows him to satisfy his scientific curiosity in striving for worth-while results and incidentally does much, at a critical period, to preserve his morale.

My direct collaborators, who in the course of training have acquired technical skill of high order, who have met and overcome the obstacles which fresh exploration almost surely presents, who have extended the ideas they have worked upon and have proved themselves able to engage independently in extending knowledge have been for me a source of deep satisfaction. A partial measure of the influence that has affected them is their persistence in research as they have gone to their own responsibilities. To look away and see disciples pushing onward in new directions and in turn initiating their young collaborators into scholarly careers is indeed a rich reward.

# CHAPTER IX

# WHEN SCIENTISTS DISAGREE

THE FIRST experience of having his statements questioned is likely to prove a painful surprise to the young investigator in science. He has tried to observe carefully, to examine critically what he has observed, and to describe as accurately as possible his methods and his results. He has been innocent of any attempt to distort the facts as he has learned them or to mislead anyone who consults his record. In these circumstances a publication which fails to confirm his work or which criticizes it comes as a shock.

As an experienced investigator I have seen not a few instances during my career that have revealed the possibilities of mistakes even after the most careful precautions have been taken. All venturesome scientists are aware of the many chances of going astray as they enter a new field. Michael Faraday, a prince of experimenters, testified "that I may be largely wrong I am free to admit—who can be right altogether in physical science which is essentially progressive and corrective?" If Faraday could feel thus toward experimentation in the realm of physics, how much readier to acknowledge the possibility of error should be an investigator who labors in the more complex and difficult realm of biology.

When a mistake has been made or when there has been failure to observe facts which perhaps should have been observed and these defects are discovered by another, the rectifying discoverer quite naturally and properly has a feeling of elation because he has contributed to the truth. But the announcement of the corrective observation or the criticism of the erroneous report can be so expressed as to cause deep hurt. Any aspersions, any slurs cast upon the skill or ability or the personal uprightness of the man whose work is being corrected are sure to stir resentment. And the use of a position of authority to impress a censorious judgment is highly reprehensible.

Some of the unfortunate features of a polemic were illustrated in the criticism of Oliver Wendell Holmes, long professor of anatomy and physiology in the Harvard Medical School, by Meigs, a Philadelphia obstetrician. Holmes early in his career had presented evidence that child-bed fever "is so far contagious as to be frequently carried from patient to patient by physicians and nurses." Meigs contemptuously commented on the foolish suggestion of "some scribblers" and declared that he was not disturbed by the opinion of "very young gentlemen"; further he appealed to prejudice in suggesting that his readers "disregard the jejune and fizzenless terms of sophomore writers who thunder forth denunciations and would mark, if they might, with a black and ineffaceable spot, the hard-won reputation of every physician who, in the province of God, is called upon to contend with the rage of one of the most destructive of epidemics." Instead of looking at the evidence directly and weighing it judicially, Meigs declared that he preferred to attribute cases of child-bed fever "to accident or Providence, of which I can form a conception, rather than to a contagion, of which I cannot form any clear idea."

In commenting on Meigs, Holmes declared that there was no epithet in the vocabulary of slight and sarcasm which could reach his own sensibilities in such a controversy and that a disrespectful phrase need be noticed only when it "may turn the student aside from the examination of evidence by discrediting or disturbing the witness." Whether it will have that effect will depend in part on the quality of the witness. Evidently Holmes was not much depressed by the derogatory comments that Meigs published. On the other hand Semmelweis, who almost simultaneously with Holmes produced proof of the contagiousness of puerperal fever, was so persistently and so scathingly denounced by his medical contemporaries that he died in tragic circumstances, a broken man.

Men differ greatly in their manner of meeting criticism and reacting to it. Huxley found controversy the spice of life. He once testified that a polemic was as little abhorrent to him "as gin to a reclaimed drunkard." And a published reply from an opponent evoked the testimony that it "caused such a flow of bile that I have been the better for it ever since." All men do not enjoy, however, what Huxley called a "public war dance." Some are sensitive and shy; they prefer to live and work in retirement. Darwin, so a close friend remarked, "never could or would defend himself." And Dixon, an English pharmacologist, who was one of the early workers on the chemical agent operating between nerve terminals and muscles, published a significant observation in a very obscure medical journal because, as he testified later, after the importance of the subject had been disclosed, he feared the criticism of his contemporaries.

It is clear, therefore, that polemics may have definitely unfortunate effects. The published results and conclusions of one or other of the contestants may in all fairness have to be acknowledged as incorrect or incomplete. Feelings of pride and professional prestige then enter the situation. In the effort to "save face" the discussion may degenerate into emphasis on minor points which have little meaning relative to the main difference at issue. Furthermore, just because there has been a controversy, doubt about the reliability of evidence may persist for a long period after the debated question has been definitely settled. With persistence of partisan feeling, facts may have their values misinterpreted or the interpretations may be so influenced by prejudice that the facts are really misconstrued. Still another unfortunate result of a continued polemic is the piling up of already mountainous literature with contentious matter, sometimes acrimonious, and the filling of many pages which could well be used for better purposes.

A fund which would permit men, who in their scientific studies obtain discrepant results, to work together in one or the other's laboratory until reasons for the discrepancies are learned would provide an immense improvement on the present method of shooting scientific papers at one another. And there might appear unpredictable values resulting from the co-operation of earnest men with ideas, skill, and knowledge of technique because something new might arise from the contacts.

The baneful features of controversy develop chiefly, I believe, from the use of language which expresses emotional attitudes rather than intellectual considerations. If differences between investigators are discussed strictly on the intellectual level there is no reason for the development of a sense of injury, no reason for later enmity. Properly conducted, a polemic may leave both the original investigator and his critic with the conviction that they have been concerned only with the advancement of science. The desire for conquest, the impulse to engage in triumphal exaltation is absent. Also the emphasis on observed facts may lead to further work of a more refined character, and thus to new and unanticipated discoveries.

During my long experience in physiological research I have had my share of controversy. For about a decade there was a sharp difference of testimony between the group working at the Harvard Physiological Laboratory, on the one side, and two physiologists of Cleveland, Ohio, in the opposition. Some of the general considerations just reviewed are illustrated by the differences which were the subject of that protracted conflict and by the manner in which it was conducted.

The Harvard group sustained the view that secretion into the blood stream from the medulla of the adrenal glands is much increased whenever there is widespread activity of the sympathetic division of the involuntary or the autonomic nervous system—for example, in conditions of asphyxia, pain, and great emotional excitement. Our critics, on the other hand, contended that the secretion from the adrenals is constant and unvarying and they found fault with the methods employed in the Harvard Laboratory. It is noteworthy that they had confirmed earlier evidence of increased discharge of adrenaline when sympathetic nerves are stimulated *electrically,* and they recognized that in asphyxia, pain, and excitement these nerves are stimulated *physiologically.* Nevertheless, they declared that their method of study, which they regarded as reliable because it was quantitative, proved that asphyxia, pain, and excitement do not increase the constant adrenaline output.

One hears relatively little of this conflict now. Through the decades and from many quarters of the world, investigators have confirmed the evidence and conclusions reported by the Harvard group. In spite of confirmations, however, for years an impression persisted that because conditional control of adrenal secretion was once in question it continued to be in question. This is an incidental point. It bears, however, on the effect of controversy on the development of science.

The criticism of the original method used by the Harvard group in demonstrating increased adrenal secretion was met by showing that the method was reliable, though rough. To confirm the earlier results we devised a new method which was much more precise—use of the denervated heart. The heart, deprived of all connections with the central nervous system, is then functionally connected with the rest of the body only through the blood vessels and the blood stream. The organ is remarkably free from any influences of a physical nature but is exquisitely sensitive to circulating adrenaline, beating faster when adrenaline is increased by as little as one part in 1,400,000,000 parts of blood. The contriving of the denervated heart was one of the valuable results of the controversy, for later it proved to be highly useful in revealing important processes in the bodily economy.

Controversy, however, may have harmful consequences. One of these may be neglect of unfavorable evidence. By use of the denervated heart Carrasco-Formiguera and I reproduced the conditions under which our critics had confirmed the testimony that sympathetic nerves, when *electrically* stimulated, augment adrenal secretion. Instead of exciting these nerves electrically, however, we used the natural stimulation, which results from asphyxia and which our critics declared had no influence on the adrenals. Our results were positive—the heart beat more rapidly. Obviously the logic of the dilemma thus presented required either acceptance of the observations of asphyxial increase of the secretion or repudiation of the observations that the output of adrenaline is under sympathetic government. That dilemma the Cleveland group did not recognize. It is a good instance of neglect of adverse evidence.

Again, Sataké and his collaborators at Sendai, Japan, who for many years employed the method used by the Cleveland physiologists, confirmed the observations made by the Harvard group. They reported that the greater amounts of adrenaline discharged from the adrenals in different circumstances were closely equivalent to the amounts we had quantified in the same circumstances by using the denervated heart.

In the tangle of conflicting claims, however, truth and error are likely to be confused. For example, in a volume entitled *The Adrenals* published in 1936, the output of adrenaline as estimated by use of the denervated heart was compared with the output as estimated by the Sataké school. Our figures were said to be fifty times as great as those given by the Japanese. As remarked above, there was in fact close agreement between the results obtained by us and those obtained by the Sendai workers, when the experimental circumstances were the same, e.g., when stimulation of a sensory nerve causes reflex secretion. Obviously the author could not have been referring to a comparison of the adrenal secretion that results from stimulating a sensory nerve because in that respect there was good agreement in the two laboratories. He was, in fact, but without explanation, contrasting figures obtained under quite different conditions. The Japanese had devised a method which allowed tapping the adrenal veins of an animal lying perfectly quiet, without anesthesia. In these circumstances they found that the discharge of adrenaline from both glands was infinitesimal—0.07 of a thousandth of a milligram (!) per kilogram of body weight per minute. What we had found when a *sensory nerve* was stimulated was, to be sure, about fifty times this extremely small output. The faulty comparison of the amounts of adrenaline secreted in quite diverse circumstances may considerately be excused in view of the long and involved conflict of testimony.

Controversy is harmful not only when it results in neglect of unfavorable evidence, confusion, and misjudgment; it may cause a certain blindness to the significance of facts which are quite evident and which invite further study. It is as if a contestant paid attention only to those features of experience which, at the moment, serve a polemical purpose.

We had noted that, after exclusion of activity of the adrenals, sensory stimulation caused a slight increase of the rate of the denervated heart. Our critics, however, observed in the same conditions that there might be a very considerable increase. This, they declared, was obviously due to increase of blood pressure. Many years previously a number of physiologists had reported that the isolated heart is not affected by increase of blood pressure. The faster rate, therefore, must have been due to some other agent. We set to work to learn what this other agent might be and found that it was a substance given off from the liver to the circulating blood. This observation, made in 1921, offered the first evidence for the existence of *sympathin,* a substance which, as shown by later experiments, comes away in the blood stream from structures stimulated by sympathetic nerve impulses. Our critics had had before them the chance of being pioneers in opening to experimentation the fascinating field of chemical mediation of nerve impulses—a chance of which they failed to take advantage.

Thus far I have laid stress on the harm which may result from scientific controversy. But the example just cited indicates that such controversy may have value. The unexpected utility of the denervated heart is illustrative. We devised this heart as a result of controversial criticism, in order to obtain additional and confirmatory facts regarding conditions which excite adrenal secretion. It demonstrated that if the adrenal glands are intact and are normally supplied with their sympathetic nerves, every condition which results in a generalized discharge of sympathetic impulses causes an accelerated heart beat. After discharge from the adrenal glands and the liver has been abolished by severing their nerve supply under surgical anesthesia, the immediate, quick, large increase of the rate (e.g., 70-90 extra beats per minute) due to excitement, for example, wholly disappears. There is, however, a belated and less marked augmentation of the rate (about 30 extra beats per minute) which appears and reaches a peak about three minutes after momentary excitement. The phenomenon occurred so regularly that it challenged explanation. Our search for the cause of this belated faster pulse was long and tedious. Only after the sympathetic system had been completely removed by careful surgery did the phenomenon vanish. Then we could either study the physiology of a new type of organism that had been produced in the world, a well-developed mammal quite deprived of supposedly necessary sympathetic nerves, or we could try to discover what had vanished, i.e., what makes the denervated heart beat faster when, in the absence of known accelerating agents, sympathetic impulses are excited.

The first of these alternatives we chose for immediate attention. The general results of researches on animals without any sympathetic system was a gradual support of the concept, previously noted, that the system acts as the governor of steady states in the organism. Such animals live for years quite comfortably in the protected and favorably conditioned confines of the laboratory, but when they are subjected to stress—to cold, heat, reduced oxygen in the air, or reduced blood sugar—they show their defects. The evidence clearly indicated that on sympathetic impulses depend maintenance of uniformity of body temperature, preservation of the slightly alkaline reaction of the blood, protection against the dangers of low blood sugar, and other related functions likely to be disturbed by alterations in the environment or by internal changes due to muscular work. The agency made up of the sympathetic system and the adrenal medulla, working conjointly, is in short the means for keeping the fairly stable state, i.e., the homeostasis, of the body fluids when that state is in jeopardy.

The second of the alternative opportunities was set aside until researches on stable states had been well advanced. We then turned our attention to the mysterious factor which, after adrenal and hepatic influences had been excluded, caused the belated acceleration of the denervated heart and which disappeared after total removal of the sympathetic system. In many experiments we found that stimulating the sympathetic nerves of any region—not only the liver but also the smooth muscle of the tail or of the gastrointestinal tract, for example—would induce the slowly developing faster heart beat. Shutting off the blood flow through a region while it was being stimulated deferred the effect on the heart until the circulation was restored. Evidently there was produced in the parts subjected to sympathetic nerve impulses a substance which, carried in the circulating blood, was able to make the heart pulsate more rapidly. Such was the method first used in proving the existence of sympathin. A long series of investigations ensued; these were summarized in a volume written by Arturo Rosenblueth, an able young Mexican physiologist, and myself and published under the title *Autonomic Neuro-Effector Systems.*

Numerous researches have been conducted in this country and abroad based on observations of animals from which the sympathetic system had been removed and numerous other researches have been conducted in this country and abroad on the nature and action of sympathin. What I wish to emphasize is that the operation of complete sympathectomy and the discovery of sympathin were consequences of a polemic. The controversy with the Cleveland physiologists required, for rebuttal, not argument but new facts. In order to obtain new facts the denervated heart was contrived and utilized. And when the denervated heart showed an altered behavior after removal of the adrenal glands, there were revealed unexpected phenomena which invited investigation. The possibilities up to this stage were disclosed equally to both parties in the controversy. If we had not accepted them on the intellectual level, as facts requiring explanation, we should not have discovered what we did.

It is most important, therefore, that a controversy be kept clear of narrowness and prejudice and that remarks should be excluded which rouse personal grievances. Contentions should be restricted sharply to the factual plane. I may cite a commendable example. In referring to a controversy with J. S. Haldane about the mode of passage of oxygen through the thin walls of the minute air sacs in the depths of the lungs Joseph Barcroft wrote:

At times I have heard persons speak as though there was some inherent absurdity in Haldane's theory and as though it were intellectually unworthy of the great man who pinned his confidence to it. Up to the point to which I have brought the reader let me convince him that I am quite out of sympathy with such statements. It seems to me a very good theory. . . . The question in my mind, when Haldane's theory took the form which I have described, was not whether the theory was a good one but whether it was really supported by the facts.

In these words Barcroft expressed an admirable spirit and attitude toward one who differed with him. It was by search for new evidence, which resulted in additions to scientific knowledge, that Barcroft and his collaborators answered the claims of Haldane. When differences between investigators result in fresh efforts to learn the truth, in refinements of technical processes, in more discriminating experiments, in more alert attention to questioned phenomena, in more cautious inferences—instead of what Harvey, the father of modern physiology, called "petty disputation"—I believe that a polemic may do more good than harm.

Not all investigators would agree with me. Probably many would take the attitude that the facts will ultimately speak for themselves, that "truth is mighty and will prevail"—and let the situation stand and wait. Faraday, whom I regard as an ideal man of science, strongly deprecated controversy. He wrote, "I have felt myself not unfrequently misunderstood, often misrepresented, sometimes passed by . . . but it is only in cases where moral turpitude has been implied, that I have felt called upon to enter on the subject in reply." When there has been clear failure, however, to employ reliable methods and to justify conclusions and when in consequence error is slipping into the "beautiful edifice of scientific truth," a crusading spirit seems to me appropriate, expressed in acts to protect that edifice.

# CHAPTER X

# SOME WORKING PRINCIPLES

HERE I am concerned with certain beliefs I hold regarding the nature of bodily organization and with inferences which may be drawn from them; also with suggestions which these beliefs offer concerning other types of organization, particularly the organization of human society.

My first article of belief is based on the observation, almost universally confirmed in present knowledge, that what happens in our bodies is directed toward a useful end. In finding new processes, therefore, we are justified in looking further for their utility. And in the search for utility new discoveries may result. The view that there are organic adjustments which promote bodily welfare, and consequently are useful, involves the conception that these activities are *directed,* i.e., that the parts operate *teleologically* for the good of the entire group of parts that constitute the organism. It may be urged that this conception is inconsistent with the idea that the province of science is strictly description. It turns away from "how" to "why" and thus may enter the realm of speculation. Many scientists hesitate openly to take that step. As the German physiologist, E. von Bruecke, remarked, "Teleology is a lady without whom no biologist can live. Yet he is ashamed to show himself with her in public."

Since a response in the organism has certain definite consequences, however, we should frankly regard them as being integrated with what has immediately preceded them. The various stages in the response that lead to the consequences may then be looked upon as *purposive.* If a crumb lodges in the larynx, for example, nerve impulses pass to the lower brain stem and, reflexly, impulses are discharged to abdominal muscles so that a cough results and the crumb is expelled. The sensory and neuromuscular sequences of the reflex action are all meaningless unless the aim is considered, unless attention is paid to the end effect toward which the complicated act is directed.

What evidence have we that the teleological concept, i.e., that organs are made to react for the good of the organism as a whole, is generally true? Can the concept be helpful and reliable in suggesting physiological experiments? It will be possible to illustrate only certain phases of the answer to this question, to point out their significance, their value, and their limitations.

Many years ago I was attempting to learn whether there is not, as a consequence of chewing and swallowing agreeable food, an increased contraction of the muscles of the stomach, a "psychic tone," favorable to the churning movements of that organ, just as there is in these circumstances a "psychic secretion" of gastric juice for promoting the digestive process. Instead of finding that the gastric muscles are contracted by swallowing, we found that there is a temporary relaxation. The relaxation is very nicely related to the time required for the passage of the swallowed food along the esophageal tube; as the food mass approaches the stomach, intragastric pressure is reduced to zero and hence the muscle of the esophagus meets no opposition. And as soon as it has pushed the food into the stomach the gastric muscles contract again and continue their churning function under restored pressure—a pretty illustration of internal adjustment for avoidance of muscular antagonism. It was just the sort of arrangement that a clever mechanic would devise. Now to the point. Thirteen years before our observation J. N. Langley, an English physiologist, had shown that electrical stimulation of a vagus nerve (distributed to the stomach) produces precisely the change which we had observed. Its neat significance was not perceived, however, because its useful pertinence to the interaction between the esophagus and the stomach was not appreciated.

There is another part of the alimentary tract of lower animals in which opposition between two muscular actions is possible. Where the small intestine empties its final contents into the large intestine, reversed waves in the muscular walls of the large intestine could oppose the entrance of the material. Immediately after discovery of the receptive relaxation of the stomach, we took the hint and paid attention to what occurs when a mass is being pushed into the large intestine. Promptly we found that in these circumstances there is a receptive relaxation of the large intestine.

Another illustration of the value of a teleological concept for making discoveries appeared early in my investigations on emotional stoppage of the activities of the alimentary tract. This interference with the beneficent services of the digestive functions did not occur if certain nerves were severed. Indeed, at the time, the arrest of digestion seemed to me merely a perverse interference with an essential process. I was ready to advocate severance of the nerves which spoiled the necessary means of nourishing the body. Further study of other effects of emotional excitement revealed, however, that it is attended by an increase of adrenaline in the circulating blood and also by an increase of blood sugar. The greater concentration of sugar in the blood raised the questions—why? what is the use? It was known that sugar is the common source of muscular energy. Powerful emotions—for example, fear and rage—are likely to be attended by fighting or flight. The sugar, set free from storage in the liver, would be useful in these possibly supreme efforts.

Why then might not other responses be useful also? That query led us to further research which brought forth evidence that the adrenaline discharged from the adrenal medulla would abolish in a few moments the effects of muscular fatigue and would greatly accelerate the speed of clotting in blood. Furthermore, injections of adrenaline showed that it had greater contractile effects on the blood vessels of the abdominal organs than elsewhere, so that the blood in excitement would be re-distributed: it would be sent away from the digestive canal and its attendant glands to flow in greater volume in the brain and in active muscles. As will be remembered, these are changes which I interpreted as being directly valuable to the organism in strife or in the consequences of strife. Now I regarded in a new light the inhibition of digestive activity by emotional excitement; it was an interruption of a process which is not essential in a life-or-death emergency and which uses a supply of blood urgently needed elsewhere. In this teleological view the stoppage of digestive activities is only a small part of the general picture; they are stopped because the useful blood flowing to the stomach and intestines is, for the time, needed in other organs which may be actually essential for continued existence. These adjustments are as much ingrained in the nervous constitution of each of us as are the simpler reflexes. They can be regarded as "purposive" in the same sense as sneezing, coughing, and vomiting are purposive. They are all responses which protect against possible harm.

There are many adaptive or useful or teleological adjustments which organisms make as individuals. Only a few illustrations can be cited here. When a person is exposed to a reduced amount of oxygen in the air—for example by residence on high mountains—the red blood corpuscles, which transport oxygen from the lungs to the shut-away tissues of the body, are increased in number. Thus, though each corpuscle carries a lighter load, the total supply to the remote tissues is maintained. It has been shown experimentally that because of adaptive changes—increase in the number of red corpuscles, increase in the capacity of corpuscles to carry oxygen, or both these advantages—lower animals can continue living in an atmosphere that contains less than 10 per cent of oxygen, i.e., less than half the concentration at sea level. In this connection it is pertinent to note that burning alcohol is smothered when the oxygen in the air falls from about 21 to 15 per cent, and that the flame of more highly combustible ether and illuminating gas goes out when as much as 13 per cent of oxygen is present.

Other highly important adaptations, so well known that they need only be mentioned, are those that appear in the presence of infection. In the body, bacteria and bacterial toxins develop and evoke specific reactions which result in neutralizing the infective agents and protecting the total organism.

These instances of adaptive interrelations between different parts of the body, adaptive arrangements favorable to survival in the struggle for existence, and adaptive reactions against invading bacteria and injurious bacterial poisons, are merely samples. Innumerable other cases could be cited of the appropriate devices which organisms, in the course of evolution, have developed for economy and protection. All this evidence seems to me to justify, with reference to each response in the body, an inquiry into the wherefore of its appearance and into its utility. When experimenting on living animals, therefore, I believe that we may reasonably count on the possible usefulness of a response as offering suggestions which could guide the inquiry. This belief sustained me during the long controversy over adrenal secretion; I felt sure that the demonstrated nervous control of that secretion could not be utterly futile, as my opponents contended.

In considering the value of the teleology of bodily reactions I have not entertained the idea that the process involves intelligent foresight working toward a predetermined end. If a response has survival value in the struggle for existence, natural selection might account for its development and preservation. There are, however, numerous instances of adjustments which, though useful, seem to be without *survival* value. The formation of a callus on the palms when rough tools are handled and the prompt recovery from a slight bruise are good examples. Also there are adaptations to circumstances probably never experienced before, as in repair of damaged internal structures, and in an increase of red corpuscles when there is reduced oxygen in the air. These are not easy to explain by present knowledge.

Not always are the responses favorable. The process of repair of injured art is, of course, of primary importance but the connective sue which results may contract to such a degree as seriously to narrow or completely close essential orifices or passages in the body. In spite of inconsistencies, however, I am convinced that the concept of utility and purposiveness has suggestive significance in biological research and that it can be fruitful.

Another of my articles of belief, which seems so self-evident that it hardly needs stating, is that structure and function are inseparably related. This implies that peculiarities of structure are associated with corresponding peculiarities of function. Where structure is complicated function is likewise complicated. Thus, unlike my psychologist friend previously mentioned, I would not regard it necessary to assume that mental processes are associated with the functioning of the simple nerve net in the intestinal wall, and I should regard extraordinarily complicated mental processes as being reasonably associated with the extraordinarily complicated relations of nerve cells in the cerebral cortex.

Certain other articles of belief I have held are related to the maintenance of uniformity or homeostasis in the body fluids. Four of these may be mentioned:

(1) Our bodies constitute open systems engaged in continuous exchanges with our external environment. They are compounded of highly unstable material. They are subjected frequently to disturbing conditions. The maintenance of a constant state within them is in itself evidence that agencies are acting or are ready to act to maintain that constancy. The relative uniformity of blood sugar, body temperature, and a slight alkalinity of the blood may be regarded, in this view, as merely samples of the effects of nice devices at work in the organism. Further research would probably prove that similar devices are

effective in maintaining the constancy of other elements in the body fluids.

(2) If a state remains steady, it does so because any tendency toward change is automatically met by increased effectiveness of the factor or factors which resist the change. As examples, I may cite thirst when there is need of water; the discharge of adrenaline, which liberates sugar from the liver, when the concentration of sugar in the blood falls below a critical point; and the increased breathing which reduces carbonic acid when the blood tends to shift toward acidity. All these reactions become more intense as the disturbance of homeostasis becomes more pronounced and they all subside quickly when the disturbance is relieved. It is probable that similar corrective reactions appear when other steady states are endangered.

(3) The regulating system which determines homeostasis of a particular feature may comprise a number of co-operating factors brought into action at the same time or successively. This statement is well illustrated by arrangements for protection against acute fall of body temperature. First, loss of heat is checked by contraction of surface blood vessels, and by erection of hair and feathers in animals supplied with these conveniences. Then more heat is provided by discharge of adrenaline, which accelerates combustion; and finally by shivering, which is merely automatic, heat-producing, muscular exercise. These processes may be awakened in series, one after another. Such examples indicate that possibly multiple physiological agencies may be at work and should be watched for.

(4) When a factor is known that can shift a homeostatic state in one direction, it is reasonable to look for automatic control of that factor or for a factor or factors which act in the opposite direction. This postulate is really implied in the previous postulates and may be regarded as emphasizing the confident belief that homeostasis is not accidental but is a result of organized self-government and that search for the governing agencies will be rewarded by their discovery.

Elsewhere I have called attention to my belief that there are general principles of organization and that the methods of maintaining stability in the highly complex and very unstable material of which our bodies are composed may have suggestive importance in showing what might be done in the social organism to assure its stability. This idea was elaborated in an address before the American Association for the Advancement of Science in 1939. Here is not the place to enter into details. However, I may point out that, corresponding to the corrective factors which come into action in our bodies when a shift from the stable state is threatened, there is, in the social body when excesses or failures threaten, a display of what physiologists call "negative induction." This is a principle which is illustrated in the little girl's misconstruction of the old adage, "Train up a child in the way he should go." Her version was "Chain up a child and away he will go." Negative induction is revealed also in the longing for alcoholic beverages when they are prohibited. A government which becomes conservative and complacent and negligent of crying need for improvements arouses opposition of a contrary character and is deprived of office. On the other hand, the excesses of a liberal and progressive regime induce in the population the rise of an opposing conservative movement. Thus there may be seen the beginnings of homeostatic control of social conditions. It is pertinent to observe that these swings from right to left and vice versa, which produce in society as in the well-developed organism a trend toward a middle course, are possible only in a democratic form of governmental organization. A totalitarian control of population, in which all corrective factors are promptly suppressed the moment they appear, can result, and actually has resulted, in such an extreme shift in one direction that the nation is brought into danger of devastating misery and possible destruction.

Another of my beliefs is that scientific study of the nature of man and of the factors which determine his conduct will have ethical consequences. It is the inhumanity of human beings that spoils the achievements of science. To be sure, valiant efforts have been made to banish inhumanity. For thousands of generations the church has preached good will among men and yet today cruelty and injustice are flagrantly inflicted on large populations. The efforts of the church have been supported by the courts; but even the rigors of legal punishment have not proved an effective restraint on criminal actions. More recently, social agencies and organized public opinion have added their efforts. Hopefully, a society of nations engaged in agreements of nonaggression; but these agreements were impotent in preventing a global war—the greatest catastrophe the human race has yet suffered. Such are the morals of mankind.

What can be done to improve human behavior? Here is the supreme challenge. Can the methods of science be applied? They have had magnificent triumphs in giving us insight into the mysteries of the physical world and into the government of its forces; can they do likewise in the much more complex realm where the forces press which direct the actions of men? Is it not possible that the churches and the courts have been proceeding without adequate understanding of the impulses which determine conduct? Are we aware of all the ways in which the doings of man can be modified? Have we not depended too largely on speculative thinking and too little on direct and accurate studies of our ideas of human motivation? Pavlov was convinced, as he himself wrote in 1923, that "only science, exact science about human nature itself, and the most sincere approach to it by the aid of the omnipotent scientific method will deliver man from the existing darkness, and will purge him from his shame in the sphere of inter-human relations." Certain it is that there exist powerful biological factors which determine our conduct and which theorists have not perhaps taken fully into account. Only recently have investigators, using methods which have proved effective in the past, begun to try to understand and to evaluate the strength of some of the agencies which are influential in deciding what we are and what we do.

Already progress has been made. We can change the cretinous idiot into a child with normal intelligence. The adult in dementia we can restore to his former activity. Among lower animals we can select a young female, wholly oblivious of offspring offered to her for adoption, and within a few days, by appropriate treatment, we can induce in her all the tenderness and devotion characteristic of an experienced mother; she will eagerly adopt and nurture not only infants of her own species but those of other species and even the babies of her natural prey. Furthermore, it is quite possible to produce in lower animals a state in which the slightest touch, a mere caress, will invariably provoke a violent manifestation of rage; and now at will we can establish a condition in which this startling and extraordinary display of rage is completely abolished.

These are instances of what is being learned about fundamental traits common to man and his humbler relatives. They indicate possibilities of becoming acquainted with powerful agencies which may profoundly affect our dispositions and our reactions to outer circumstances. They are beginnings of efforts to acquire exact knowledge of the nature of the forces that influence conduct. On the basis of experience we must rely on knowledge, knowledge as precise as possible and not on surmise, to give us understanding of human actions and the ways of influencing them. Even if we should learn how to control human behavior, however, there would still remain the problem of guiding the desire to control it toward good rather than toward evil. A vast uncharted realm of fundamental social import lies before us awaiting exploration.

Finally, I wish to declare my belief that phenomena, no matter how mysterious they may appear to be, have a natural explanation and will yield their secrets to the persistent, ingenious, and cautious efforts of the investigator. This faith that there is no intrusion of the extranatural in the course of observed phenomena is, as a matter of fact, commonly accepted in the practical affairs of daily living. Shipping companies, business firms, insurance agencies do not as a rule count upon any but routine processes for explanation of the success or failure of their ventures. The late Dr. Morton Prince once offered five thousand dollars to anyone who, during a year, would demonstrate to a committee which he selected, any evidence of supernatural power. He asked me to serve, along with Theodore Lyman, physicist, S. Burt Wolbach, pathologist, Harlow Shapley, astronomer, and Harry Houdini, magician. The only communication we received in the twelve months of waiting came from the inmate of a hospital for mental disease who declared that if we would get him out he could win the prize! There is an inadequately recognized basis for deep satisfaction in being able to count upon the uniformities of natural events. If some whimsical *deus ex machina* could be invoked here and there to create incalculable fortuitous appearances and disappearances, we should indeed be stunned with bewilderment. We should not know what to do.

Occasionally in research very perplexing difficulties are encountered. I have previously mentioned the strange acceleration of the heart during vigorous activity and emotional excitement, after all cardiac nerves had been severed and all known stimulating agents (the adrenal glands and the liver) had been excluded from action. What could cause the more rapid beat? The effective agent must act via the blood stream. A long series of systematic experiments was required to rule out the possible influences of increased temperature, of the pancreas and other abdominal organs, of the thyroid and related glands of internal secretion, and of chemical substances which might arise from muscular contractions. Exclusion of these items singly and *in toto* did not abolish the faster cardiac pulse. But we could be sure that the effect was not due to magic! It must have an observable explanation. And persistence finally disclosed the effective agent as a substance given off from structures affected by impulses from sympathetic nerves.

Our ancestors thought themselves surrounded by baffling mystical forces—good and evil spirits which profoundly affected their lives. Such words as "lunatic" and "influenza," arising from former belief in the powers of the moon and the stars, we have in our dictionaries as a heritage of that time. As science has become more and more exact it has explained obscure processes and mysterious influences. The explanations have in fact liberated mankind from fettering superstitions and baseless fears.

# CHAPTER XI

# WAYS OF GOING ASTRAY

THE TITLE of this chapter might indicate that I planned to preach a sermon. Certainly I would not advocate going astray, nor would I point out the ways of error expecting that they would be followed. Rather, my intent is, indeed, to tell about some of the most common and most dangerous ways, in order to warn against them. As related to workers in science, the warnings have a professional significance. But many of the errors which the scientist should avoid, all of us should avoid as we deal with our fellows. The warnings, therefore, have more than a narrowly limited bearing.

First I would caution against the Error of Untested Assumption. In a previous chapter I described the controversy in which critics of the Harvard group of investigators observed an increased rate of the denervated heart when, in the absence of the adrenal glands, they stimulated the sympathetic nerves distributed to abdominal organs. Such stimulation causes a rise of blood pressure. They assumed that the faster heart rate which followed the stimulation was due to that change. They did not test this assumption; if they had done so, they would have seen that within a wide range the denervated heart is indifferent to blood-pressure changes. Because of this erroneous assumption they were led astray.

A second type of mistake may be designated the Error of the Incomplete Test. At times during the past two centuries curiosity concerning the origin of life on earth led to experiments to prove the possibility of spontaneous generation. The common method of experimenting was to place a nutrient fluid in flasks and, after subjecting the fluid to different conditions, to note whether living organisms appeared in it. Critical examination of one set of experiments by a committee of which Huxley was chairman resulted in a report that, in view of the precautions or lack of precautions against contamination, there would have been no surprise if in the cultures anything had been found, from a gold watch to a red geranium!

About the middle of the eighteenth century Needham informed the Royal Society of London that he had heated mutton gravy, placed it in a bottle which he corked, then had heated the bottle again and put it aside. At the end of a few days the liquid was swarming with animalcules. This looked like a clean proof of spontaneous generation. The Italian investigator Spallanzani was not convinced. The bottles might not have been tightly corked or they might not have been heated sufficiently long to destroy all living things or the seeds of living things. The first possibility he eliminated by sealing the necks of the glass flasks in which the culture medium was placed. The second possibility he examined by heating the sealed flasks for different lengths of time. These tests were conclusive. The flasks which had been exposed to heat for a few minutes contained animalcules; those which had been heated for an hour did not. Obviously there were organisms or seeds which were able to survive short heating but were destroyed when the heating was prolonged. Once they were destroyed there was no spontaneous generation.

Another interesting example of an incomplete experiment is found in the report of the French physiologist, Flourens, regarding the effect of removal of the cerebral hemispheres from a pigeon. In Flourens' words the animal is *"condamné à un sommeil perpétuel."* Certainly the decerebrate pigeon, standing utterly still, with feathers ruffled, head withdrawn, and eyes closed has an appearance which would justify Flourens' description. This state, however, is only temporary. If he had continued his observations he would have seen the bird later become surprisingly active, walking persistently to and fro in its enclosure.

As noted in a previous chapter, failure to continue stimulation of a muscle through its nerve, after extreme muscular fatigue appeared, resulted in missing the remarkable phenomenon of recovery from the fatigued state to such a degree that the muscle, even during activity, regains most of its original ability to respond to nerve impulses.

In all foregoing instances significant facts were not detected because the experimental procedures or observations ended too soon.

The Error of Omitted Control is another and an inexcusable scientific misdemeanor. A control, in the scientific sense, is a standard of comparison used to check an inference drawn from an experiment. The biologist who was reported to have baptized one of his identical twins and kept the other as a "control" illustrates the principle, though in the story his basis for judging effects was left obscure. The Error is well illustrated by a rather extreme instance in a report of physiological experimentation, published in a highly reputable scientific periodical. The experimental procedure involved perfusion of salt solution through the blood vessels of the pancreas. A fine glass tube, inserted into the duct which leads away from that organ, showed that the pancreas was not secreting any juice. Now in another animal the nerves leading to the pancreas were stimulated and the blood coming away from it was collected during the stimulation. This blood was then used to replace the salt solution as a perfusing fluid in the vessels of the pancreas of the first animal. Soon this pancreas began to pour out a fluid through its duct. The inference was drawn that in the second animal stimulation of the pancreas by nerve impulses had evoked a chemical substance which brought the perfused pancreas into action. There is little doubt that this experiment could be repeated many times and would always give the same result. *That* criterion of a "good" experiment, therefore, is faulty; for, as long as the errors remain constant, their effects will reappear. Thus, the mere fact that a procedure can be repeated may not have any pertinence at all, because of the lack of corrective controls. At least two checks or controls were lacking in the experiment just described. First, there was no evidence that blood collected from the pancreatic vessels of the second animal, when the nerves were *not* stimulated, would not have had the same effect as the blood collected during the stimulation. Second, there was no evidence that blood taken from any other part of the body would not have had the same effect. It is possible that the cells of the pancreas perfused with salt solution were affected by the abnormal conditions (e.g., by lack of oxygen, which the solution does not carry) and that blood from any source, helpful in restoring the natural state of the cells, would result in their becoming active. Still another precaution lacking in the experiment was a test of the fluid discharged through the pancreatic duct. Even when it appeared after blood was used as a perfusate, it might not have been proper pancreatic juice; the cells may have been so seriously damaged by an inadequate delivery of oxygen to them while the salt solution was flowing that later they could not function properly.

A motto to be reverentially respected by every investigator who introduces new factors in his experiments and by every reader of reports of complex experimentation is *"cherchez le contrôle."*

Another way of going wrong is through the Error of Faulty Technique. A good example of this type occurred in experiments in which I co-operated. It is pertinent to confess that my collaborator and I felt comfortable about our observations because of previous studies by T. A. Storey. He had rapidly and repeatedly stimulated a muscle by currents derived from a revolving magneto machine and had found that the muscle, instead of contracting to a uniform extent at each stimulation, contracted to gradually increasing, then to gradually decreasing, extents in a series which recurred in rhythms or waves with crests and hollows. In our experiments, likewise, there were oscillatory variations in the extents of contraction of a muscle rhythmically and rapidly actuated by stimuli of uniform strength. The phenomenon was novel. Various conditions affecting it were carefully studied and were reported as being characteristic of the physiology of muscular performance.

A decade passed during which no one else attempted to repeat what we had done. Then the question was raised whether these same oscillations in the degree of contraction would occur in another type of muscle than that which we had examined in the former experiments. Apparatus was set up to test the idea, and to our astonishment the oscillations did not occur. This was very puzzling. Comparison of the recording devices used in the early and in the new experiments revealed one striking difference. In the early experiments the strong cord attached to the tendon of the muscle passed over a wheel and down to the writing lever. In the new experiments we attached the cord to the top of the vertical side of a rigid, triangular, metal plate which bore the writing lever on its horizontal side; the pivot of the lever was at the junction of these two sides, so that when the muscle contracted the writing point was pulled upward. What could be the possible difference between this arrangement and that in which the wheel was used? Fortunately, search brought out of storage the very wheel used in the former experiments. The muscle and the recording lever were set up as before, rapid stimulation was applied, and the oscillatory variations in records promptly reappeared! Now careful inspection revealed that when the muscle contracted vigorously the wheel was given a revolving momentum. As the muscular tension diminished near the end of a contraction, the turning wheel slipped slightly under the cord. The wheel proved to be not precisely centered. This eccentricity, not perceptible on simple examination, had an effect which was greatly magnified by the recording lever. As the wheel turned through its entire circle, therefore, differences in the height to which the writing point rose were registered up and down in the waves. The phenomena which were apparently intrinsic in the muscle were actually due to a defect in the recording apparatus.

In the earlier study, when we supposed we were dealing strictly with muscular events, we had noted that the waves appeared regularly and persisted for long periods in vigorous animals; they were not present or were present for only a brief period in weak animals. We now knew that the muscle of vigorous animals contracted energetically and gave the wheel a quick acceleration which caused slipping; they did not occur in weak animals because the contractions were too moderate to have that effect. Fatigue or a diminished blood supply was attended by a lessening of the energy of contraction. In consequence the wheel no longer slipped or it slipped to a less degree than before when the contractions were quick and powerful. The waves, therefore, vanished or became longer. When adrenaline was injected after the muscle was fatigued, the waves recurred if they had ceased or they were more frequent if they had become slow, because of the invigorating effects of adrenaline and consequent greater momentum and greater slipping of the wheel. In the earlier experiments curare was used to block effects of nerve impulses and the muscle was then stimulated directly through electrodes applied to it. When thus stimulated the waves appeared and the inference was drawn that they were of muscular origin. We now knew that they were not of muscular origin but were the consequence of the use of an eccentric wheel in the experimental arrangements.

The artificial character of the waves of variation of muscular contraction in our experiments led us to inquire into the conditions of Storey's experiments which had been published nearly a quarter of a century before. His apparatus was placed in our hands. Here again a revolving wheel was employed. It became clear that a defect in the structure of the apparatus permitted spread of the electric current to some degree from one sector to another as the armatures turned. The very slight stimulations from sparking between successive sectors after the sector had passed which gave the muscle its main stimulus resulted in a retarded relaxation and consequently in rhythmic recurrences of waves of response.

Lord Lister once remarked, "Next to the promulgation of truth, the best thing I can conceive that a man can do is the recantation of a public error"—a remark with which I thoroughly agree. Of course, as promptly as possible I published the explanation of the oscillatory contractile variations of rhythmically stimulated muscle. The paper ended with the statement that our experience "should be useful as a warning to *beware of wheels* in apparatus for stimulating or recording." A warning of still wider import which I now strongly emphasize is "Always make sure that your technical devices do not deceive you."

A not uncommon mistake in judging a complicated situation results from Neglect of Multiple Causes. The error is committed when an experimenter removes an agent which might be active in a process and, on noting that the process continues, draws the conclusion that the agent was not involved. Our bodies have various ways of reaching the same end. Shivering alone can prevent the bodily temperatures from falling; that does not prove that other factors which have been prevented from operating are ordinarily useless. I once had to defend the role of adrenaline as a means of calling forth sugar from storage in the liver. It is true that after the adrenal medulla has been excluded, the usual sugar concentration in the blood is maintained. Drawing the conclusion that adrenaline secretion, therefore, exerts "no important function" is an instance of Neglect of Multiple Causes. Sugar can be discharged from the liver reserves in other ways—by sympathin or merely because the concentration in the blood is falling—but never with the speed and effectiveness seen when adrenaline is acting. ·

A serious error investigators can make, as previously noted, is that of drawing inferences or stating conclusions which go beyond what is justifiable from the observed facts. This may be called the Error of Unwarranted Conclusions. It is likely to creep in when there are theoretical and doctrinaire interests which bias the investigator's judgment. A good illustration of this type of error may be taken from psychology. Weber studied the increase of the stimulus at different levels that is necessary for producing the smallest noticeable change of sensation. He came to the conclusion that the increase of the stimulus, barely recognized as being greater, bears a constant ratio to that originally acting. Thus, if an ounce must be added to a pound in order to make a just perceptible difference in the sensation of weight, not one ounce but about ten ounces must be added to ten pounds if a change in sensation is to be felt. This so-called "Weber's law" varies in its applicability to different sensations. Also, it does not hold at small or at great intensities, though for a median range it expresses an approximate relation.

Fechner, however, took Weber's results and formulated what he regarded as a more precise and quantitative "law." It assumed that there are units of sensation and stated that in order to produce equal steps of perceptible increases of sensation there must be present equal ratios of increasing stimulation, or in more technical terms, the intensity of the sensation is approximately proportionate to the logarithm of the strength of the stimulus. This sounds learned and appears to be exact—but it is not true! Every sensation is itself a unity; though stimuli may be composite, sensations are not—they cannot be regarded as masses of combined units. And the proper psychological consequence of Fechner's "law," in James's opinion, "is just *nothing*." Entire libraries on psychophysics bear witness to patient devotion to studies based on this erroneous "law." Herrick remarks, "The error of psychophysics remains monumentally instructive."

There are other, minor mistakes which an inexperienced investigator may make and against which he may be cautioned. I can testify regarding some of these mistakes from my own experience. Among them is that of Neglected Detail. In the first X-ray observations on the movements of the stomach and intestines, bismuth subnitrate was used as the insoluble salt which, when mixed with the food, renders the contents of the stomach and intestines opaque to the rays and thereby throws visible shadows on a glowing screen. I used other heavy insoluble salts, among them barium sulphate. I did not mention that fact, however, but merely made a general statement. Now the safer barium sulphate is employed instead of bismuth salts; it might have been employed much earlier if I had specified the salts I tested. Again, in the argument in favor of a toxic factor as the occasion for the appearance of shock in wounded men I called attention to evidence indicating a release of poisonous substances from the badly torn tissues. There was, indeed, the possibility that toxins might be derived from disintegrating structures, damaged by the flying missiles of warfare. In all war wounds, however, there is bacterial infection. It is well known that the growth of bacteria in dead or dying tissues is likely to produce toxins. The role of bacterial toxins in the production of shock was mentioned in the article, but the main emphasis was laid on possible poisons from tissue breakdown. That was an error of neglect of the important factor of infection.

Another mistake of the inexpert is that of heading a paper with an Improper Title. The title should include as many words as are necessary to indicate what the paper contains. Since an index of scientific literature will record the title under various headings, the variety of words will supply to searchers in the literature clues to the work the author has done. A paper ought to describe only observations which are implied in the title. Of my earliest publications one was "The Movements of the Stomach Studied by Means of the Röntgen Rays." In it I reported that as more and more food is swallowed the new masses are pressed into the food already in the stomach so that there is a stratification, which is only gradually destroyed as the peristaltic waves churn the gastric contents. Some years later a German investigator described the primary stratification of food in the stomach. Thus, even though the specific naming of his observations gave him proper credit, he lost time by repeat ing work already done. If a result has been obtained that is not pertinent to the general subject under consideration, it is better to withhold it and to add other related results before giving it publicity. When included in an account of studies foreign to it, it is fairly certain to be lost.

Investigators of the functions of higher organisms are concerned with extremely complicated processes. Not only are there complex interrelations among the processes participating in the life of these organisms but also the organisms themselves are responsive to external conditions imposed upon them, conditions which may further confuse the total situation. Moreover, the technical methods employed in attempting to elucidate the events which are taking place may themselves be misleading unless the utmost care is exercised to assure absence of defects. The need for the most scrupulous and cautious critical judgment in conducting experiments is indicated in the pessimistic testimony of Darwin, who declared, "nature will tell you a direct lie if she can." Of the many sorts of error that may creep into experimental procedures, I have considered and illustrated a few which have seemed to me most important.

By carefully avoiding untested assumptions, then, by making sure that an experiment is carried through to the end, by invariably insisting on adequate controls, by meticulously examining apparatus for possible defects, by scrupulously attending to a close fit of conclusions to observed facts, the investigator may hope to avoid errors. And if, in reporting methods and results, pertinent details are not neglected and the paper is given a title that properly defines the contents, he may feel that he has done his best to tell the truth.

# CHAPTER XII

# A PARENTHESIS OF WAR

In 1917, when the United States entered World War I, there was a common desire among scientific investigators to do everything possible to aid in the war effort. Word had come from England that one of the most serious problems of war surgery was that of dealing with wound shock, a condition, long mysterious, that is seen on a huge scale in warfare. The problem could be attacked by physiological methods and a group of American physiologists was organized to work on it. There was a similar group in England, including Henry H. Dale, Charles S. Sherrington, Ernest H. Starling, and William M. Bayliss. When the Harvard Hospital Unit was formed I decided to accompany it and to serve in France as a field investigator who would report back to the laboratory workers the shock phenomena presented by badly wounded men. The decision required a sharp break with all my previous habits. I must cease to be a laboratory hermit and go forth into the world for scientific study. I must turn from observations on natural processes in lower animals to observations on grievously torn and battered human beings. And I must leave the peace and security of academic circles and enter the turmoil and distress and the excitements of battle areas. All these novelties made a profound impression on me, not only as a converted investigator, but as a citizen eager for victory of our arms. When the war was over I returned, in 1919, to the researches I had abandoned. The experiences during the two-year interval were sequestered; they formed a sort of parenthesis in the routine course of university responsibilities. Letters written home and some published articles recorded the many events of the intrusive period. A few of these events I have selected to tell of here.

The Harvard Hospital Unit included physicians and surgeons of skill and eminence—among them Harvey Cushing, Roger I. Lee, Robert B. Osgood, Joseph C. Aub, and O. H. Robertson. We left New York early in May, 1917, and after a week in London were sent to a hospital at Dannes-Camiers, not far from Boulogne. At Boulogne was an old friend of mine, Colonel T. R. Elliott, who represented in France the English Medical Research Committee. He had been informed that I wished to investigate directly conditions attending wound shock, as manifested in the seriously wounded. In the old town of Béthune, at that time, there was a small group interested in shock problems; that seemed, therefore, the most favorable place for my purposes.

Colonel Elliott telephoned to General Pike, the chief medical officer of the British army which governed Béthune, to ask whether I might be permitted to enter that area. In order to certify me as an investigator he explained to the general that I had invented the bismuth meal. General Pike replied, "Send him along! Send him along! I had to take a bismuth meal once and I'd like to knock him down." Far from knocking me down, General Pike was most gracious and helpful; and General Cuthbert Wallace, who was chief surgeon, did everything possible to make the work at Béthune effective.

While waiting for departure of the coach which was to take me toward the front, a troop train near by was being loaded; the soldiers, burdened with their heavy kits, were climbing into the little cars marked "Chevaux 8, Hommes 40." A company of Scots arrived, marching after four bagpipes which shrilled out their weird music. Some of them were singing *Loch Lomond*. The words, "Ye'll tak' the high road, and I'll tak' the low road, and I'll be in Scotland afore ye," had a possible grim symbolism. And when they sang "Me and my true love will never meet again," it wrung my heart. They were going up the line for a "push" and many would never return.

Béthune was a picturesque old town which still retained in its architecture evidences of the time when the Spaniards occupied that part of Flanders. In a large seminary building, about five miles from the front line, was Number 33 Casualty Clearing Station. There only the badly wounded, who had to be cared for as soon as possible, were allowed to remain. On the professional staff of the Clearing Station were Captain John Fraser, the surgeon, and Captain A. N. Hooper, physician, who for some time had been interested in the phenomena of shock. Closer to the line and co-operating with them was Captain E. M. Cowell (later Major General Cowell of the British Army Medical Corps).

In Béthune, at almost any time of the day or night, we could hear the distant thumps of the heavy guns. From the upper windows of the seminary we could look away to the east, over the level fields, to where the fighting was in progress. One night, gazing out through the darkness, I watched an intense bombardment. Airplanes were humming under the clouds, dropping red and blue signal flares. Hostile searchlights threw their powerful pencils hither and thither, searching out these sky scouts and bombers; and when the planes were discovered, chains of flaming incendiary bombs ("flaming onions") were shot at them through the confused sky. All these illuminations, added to the Very lights, and to the incessant roar and the flashes of the thundering guns made a scene so awful that it seemed to me almost beyond belief that in the midst of it were *men,* with eyes and ears and sensitive nerves, who were being ripped open and mangled as they endured the maelstrom of tumult and terror.

About mid-August an attack in the line north of Lens gave me my first major experience of the horrors of a shock ward. The attack had been made by Canadians. Among the seriously wounded were Swedes from Winnipeg, an Indian, a Japanese, and some French from Montreal who spoke broken English. Clay covered their shoes until they were rounded lumps of mud; it plastered their puttees and trousers or clung to them in hanging masses; it smeared their hands and faces; and it stuck in their hair. No wonder they were badly infected by missiles passing through this corrupted stuff before reaching the flesh. And blood! It was everywhere. It reddened the bandages. It lay in jellied masses on the stretchers. Hands, used to stop the bleeding, were streaked and blotched with blood. It had streamed over their tunics and trousers—indeed, their clothes were sometimes nearly covered with gore.

Their wounds were appalling. A big man with his jaw partly shot away sat, with a great mass of bandages around his head, drooling blood into a cup. Two were shot through the urinary bladder. Another, an officer, had a considerable part of his liver out under the bandage. The head of the Japanese was completely covered, except eyes, nostrils and mouth; his lips were black and swollen to an enormous size, and his eyelids were puffed till they were quite shut. Another head case was utterly grotesque; the soldier had evidently been peppered with flying bits of mud and steel, the cheeks and lips and eyelids were so swollen that the whole head under the stretched gauze had the shape of a squat pear, with no prominences. Only his bruised lips were exposed and he seemed near death; but when I felt his pulse, it was good and he muttered the universal call for water.

Extra surgeons were there to help. Even so, it was impossible to care for the urgent cases promptly. By next morning thirteen of about sixty of the badly wounded had died. The officer with the liver wound was delirious when I went to him. He wished to get up and walk about for a while. Then he looked at me wanly and said that he was very tired and needed a week in the woods. Shortly thereafter the orderlies passed by with his body, covered reverently with the British flag. A poor wretch who became delirious thought that all the attendants in the wards were Germans. And whenever anyone approached him he would struggle up and, extending his arms, as if holding his rifle, would shout, "Get out! Bang! You're dead!" Then, exhausted, he would sink back and whisper, "It's no use, they're too much for me." Soon he, too, was gone.

The shock ward at night was a harrowing place. Only a dim light was permissible because of hostile airplanes. In the near-darkness we could see the tossing, restless forms and hear the groans and moans, the frequent sounds of vomiting, and the cries, "Oh, doctor, let me sleep," and "Water, I must have water." A prompt ejection of the swallowed water, when it is given to men in shock, is commonly a part of their torment.

Evidence accumulated that in the badly wounded brought to the clearing station the normal, slightly alkaline condition of the blood is changed toward an acid reaction. A soldier with his left knee shattered, his right calf torn open, half of his right hand mashed, and a ghastly rip in his right forearm was operated upon. After the operation his blood pressure, instead of being about 115 millimeters of mercury, was 68. His pulse, instead of being about 80 beats per minute, was 148. And his respiration, instead of being 15 or 20 breaths per minute, was 34. Soon he was much worse. The respirations, which most clearly tell the tale of accumulating acid in the blood, were more than 40 per minute. It was an emergency case and I suggested that we inject into the blood stream a solution of sodium bicarbonate. By the time we had it ready he was gasping for breath; the respiratory rate had risen to 48. In spite of his wounds he lifted himself on his elbow crying out between gasps, "I can't breathe." "Give me air." "I can stick the pain, but I must have air." We ran 35 ounces of the warm soda solution into an arm vein. The change which occurred was dramatic. His respirations promptly fell from 48 to 26 per minute and his pulse from 148 to 126. In ten minutes he was quietly sleeping. Another similar crisis about six hours later was met in the same manner; the next day his blood pressure gradually rose to 86, 102, 114 millimeters of mercury, and he sat in his slanting bed, smoking a cigarette, with much satisfaction.

Other cases like this, treated with soda, displayed the same dramatic effect. The results were so striking that we thought we had found the proper method of dealing effectively with wound shock. Our enthusiasm, however, was premature for, in many cases, the effects proved to be only temporary. The studies on wounded men at Béthune disclosed the fact that the degree of the "acidosis," with which we had been dealing, is closely related to the degree of impairment of the circulation, i.e., it is a late, secondary phenomenon and that it can be avoided if the primary harmful condition is treated promptly. The primary condition is an inadequate supply of oxygen to the tissues because of deficient circulation of blood; and the deficient circulation, as shown by fellow workers on the problem, mainly by Norman Keith and his associates, is due to a reduced volume of blood in the circulatory system. If the volume is soon restored so that the circulation and the oxygen delivery are made adequate, the acidosis and other harmful secondary phenomena do not occur. Shock from hemorrhage, burns, and severe accidents occurs in civil life. The proof that what is needed in treating it is prompt replacement of the fluid lost from the blood stream is therefore a perpetual benefit. We grasp at any gains which can be set against the appalling losses of war. Here is one.

In November, 1917, Captain Fraser and I left Béthune for England. During the subsequent three months I worked experimentally on shock at University College, London, in co-operation with the physiologist, William Bayliss. Even in London we did not avoid the direct impact of the war, for not infrequently there were bombing raids over the city. One clear, cold, starlit evening I started toward the Warren Street underground station. As I entered it, I encountered a terrific crush with guards shouting, people pushing and struggling for the lifts, and no possibility of buying a ticket. When I inquired, "What's up?" the brief answer was, "Air raid." The men at the lifts were calling out, "Women with babies only. Men down the stairs." There the women with babies were—anxious-looking mothers carrying their weeping infants and all pushing and driving against one another in their efforts to crowd into the great cages. At the top of the stairs a fierce struggle was going on; when that was passed, however, I went down quite comfortably until I approached the platform level. The lower I went, the more were the stairs used for seats. And what a motley crowd it was! Haggard old women with unrestrained gray hair, mothers with little children in their arms and others clinging to their skirts, girls wearing the finery of the family (the best way to carry it), some rather bleary-eyed old men, and irresponsible boys who took the whole affair as a lark. I heard hasty words in Italian, in French, and in Yiddish. The air reeked of garlic and dirty human bodies, and the noise of the moving trains hardly drowned the jabber of tongues. Trains came, stopped, and passed on, so crowded that I could not push into a car. At last I was able to enter one, and as it sped toward Hampstead I saw repeated at each station what I had seen at Warren Street.

While I was in London I learned that I had been elected president of the Red Cross Medical Research Society, organized by Americans for a common exchange of the experiences of French, British, and American physicians and surgeons in military service. The society was to meet in Paris once a month to discuss papers concerned with important medical problems arising in the armed forces. In March, 1918, I was transferred to Paris and, after some weeks of waiting, appointed director of a laboratory at Dijon under the genial command of Colonel J. F. Siler. My task was to continue laboratory investigations of shock and to teach groups of medical officers what we then knew of its nature and treatment; the plan was to send them to forward hospitals during a "push" to attend to the seriously wounded. With the help of McKeen Cattell, Joseph Aub, and later O. H. Robertson, I taught shock teams in weekly sessions as they were sent to Dijon for instruction.

In February I had been honored by appointment to give the

Croonian lecture of 1918 before the Royal Society. This engagement took me back to London in June, when I presented a theory of thirst and the evidence supporting it. Duties required a visit to Oxford. There I had an opportunity to see how profoundly the academic character of the ancient university was altered by the war. Sir Charles S. Sherrington, the physiologist, was investigating the spread of the poison of tetanus in the nervous system, an urgent war problem. Others were busy with questions of fatigue and efficiency among munition workers. As we passed a short street, Sherrington waved toward the houses facing it and said to me quietly, "Hardly a home in that lane is free from mourning for the loss of a son or a father." In one of the colleges I met a student who had the reputation of being exceptionally gifted; he had been totally blinded by a bullet which passed through his head, from side to side, just back of the eyes. While I was in Oxford I had occasion to meet again Sir William Osler. The death of his only son in a Flanders battle had been a shattering blow. When I told Sir William, in answer to a direct question, that I had five children, he said, "lucky man"; and when he learned that four were girls, he said, "luckier still."

Military planes droning in the sky and uniformed men occupying the colleges were continuous reminders of the dark shadow of war. And yet life was not always in shadow. From the Oslers I went to call on Professor J. S. Haldane. He too was deeply involved in war research but he suggested dropping it for a while and going to "dine in hall" at New College. To my great interest and pleasure I was seated at the right hand of the warden or master, W. A. Spooner, of spoonerism fame. He was a kindly old gentleman, an albino, colorless in hair and eyes, with a face frequently illumined with smiles. I hung on his talk expecting one of his gems, but nothing came. I had heard of his "tons of soil" in an address to working men, his toast to "our queer Dean" in honor of Victoria, and his description of an audience as composed of "tiers of beery wenches"; but Haldane told me of one that was new to me—his announcing a hymn in chapel, "We will now sing 'From Iceland's greasy mountains to India's coral strand.' " Haldane himself was an original. He was keen and ingenious in his physiological experimenting, but extraordinarily absent-minded. Once, when he and I had to wait at the Oxford platform exit while another member of our party ran to the train to recover the ticket he had left in the coach, Haldane remarked dreamily, "I never *forgot* my ticket, but I once *ate* my ticket!" It was remarkable that one so abstracted and unworldly as he was could be an intensely practical man. The mine workers have much to thank him for in the ingenious inventions he devised for their safety and security.

On returning to France I was inadvertently cast into the midst of the vast final effort of the Germans to break the French defenses. This experience gave me unusual opportunity for a near view of medical services in a battle. Early in July, 1918, a request came that I be temporarily assigned to the 42nd Division, then in the line north of Châlons-sur-Marne. There on Sunday evening, July 14, "Bastille Day," a group of us medical officers met together and sat nonchalantly conversing and discussing until nearly 10:30. The thought slipped through my mind that this might be comfortable ease before tragedy. About 10:45 we retired to our cots. At 11:50 there suddenly began the most stupendous, the most terrific, the most inconceivably terrifying roar—like Niagara behind the falls, like thousands of huge motor trucks speeding over cobblestones, like freight trains passing each other in a tunnel. It was the beginning of the great German attack. The moment the din started I jumped to my feet, and saw the whole northern horizon ablaze with flashing guns and bursting shells. The frightful din continued for four mortal hours, with occasional intensifications which made it seem to come nearer.

I had dressed at once. Scarcely had I put on my belt when there was a zip-sish-bang and a big German shell burst to the south of the hospital. We were ordered into the trenches. For

periods thereafter, shells arrived every three minutes, hitting
to the east and the west of us. At 2:30 a call came for Major
Cannon. I climbed out of the trench and hastened to the shock
ward. The first patients were some officers who had been peril-
ously wounded; soon the flood of torn men began to pour in.
We worked intensively with the shells hissing and ripping and
banging near us, and the great roar continuing in the distance.
We were utterly oblivious of passing time. About 5:30 a shell
whizzed down and exploded near by. At once we put on our
steel helmets. The shelling continued, but nothing came very
near until about six o'clock when, sish-crash, a shell struck one
of the wards. At once nurses were ordered into the dugouts and
doctors and orderlies were commanded to get the patients there
also, as soon as possible. Hardly were these motions started before I was overwhelmed by a deafening crash. A shell had
struck the ward just next to mine, not more than twenty feet
distant, and had torn off the roof. Fragments of the missile
were driven through both wooden walls of my ward and on
through the canvas of the tent beyond. Not a person in our
ward was hit. In the ward where the shell landed, however,
two patients just operated on were killed, one of them by having the top of his head blown away. The dust, smoke and gases
floated everywhere about us but we kept at our jobs. By good
fortune we succeeded, without further disturbance, in clearing
the wards and carrying all our patients to the dugouts. Again
we officers went to the trenches and remained there until about
seven o'clock, when the bombardment of the hospital appeared
to be at an end.

It was necessary to move. As soon as possible big trucks and
ambulances were made ready to carry equipment and supplies
and the wounded, about thirteen miles further south, to Écury.
On our slow journey we passed the long stream of fleeing refugees. As I think back over that trip, here are some of the im-
pressions I recall——a woman and a boy carrying gas masks and
pushing a baby carriage full of family treasures; great carts
laden with bicycles, hay, bedquilts, bread, old women, babies,

clothing; dogs and goats trotting along beside the walking people; a young girl or a middle-aged woman leading the horses, sometimes an old man leading; carts standing before the houses and people hurrying to get out their belongings—no tears or crying, no complaining; the fields rich with grain, just turning yellow and ready for the harvest, under the blue, cloud-flecked, summer sky; all nature lovely and joyous, if it were not for the hideous cruelty of war.

No sooner did I arrive at Écury than I was directed to the shock ward. It was already filled with the sickening sights associated in my memory with Béthune. Men with their bellies torn open, with the sides of their faces ripped out, with brains oozing from skull wounds, with the bladder shot through, with sucking chest wounds—such were the pathetic, well-nigh hopeless cases left in the ward. By the second day those who had not already died were likely to be weakened and septic, or restless with approaching death. Cursings, expletives, repeated shouts for "mother" or for "mama" or "papa," and the stench of purulent wounds and dressings made the shock ward a heart-rending place. As soon as a wounded man had improved and was out of danger he was removed to another, relatively quiet tent where conditions of surgical attention and care were more favorable. This selection always left in the shock ward the very worst and nearly desperate cases. It should be stated that judging the total situation by the horrifying scenes in that ward is unfair; the lightly wounded, after a battle, wander about, smoking cigarettes and comparing experiences; and most of the wounded are only lightly wounded. On the other hand, there are horrors of death and mutilation on the battlefield not seen even in the shock ward.

During my absence with the 42nd Division the shock teams coming to Dijon for instruction had gone away without full training. My services really belonged to the American Expeditionary Force and not to any special division. Consequently I was ordered to Dijon and given the commission of going thereafter to forward areas during activity to make sure that shock teams were properly equipped and were alert in caring for the wounded.

By the end of October conditions had quieted down to such a degree that I had free time. Early in November, Lieutenant Colonel Alexander Lambert, chief surgeon of the American Red Cross in France, and Lieutenant Colonel Simon Flexner, director of the Rockefeller Institute in New York City, came to Dijon. They invited me to motor with them through the country to the north, which I knew fairly well because of previous visits to forward hospitals. The object was to inspect the hospitals and to learn of possible needs. On November 10 we reached Verdun; slowly and with deep feeling we passed through that tragic and glorious place. I was reminded of the relics of the Baths of Caracalla—the bare broken walls standing somber and silent, the whole city wrecked in that fashion. From Verdun westward everywhere the roads were soupy seas of mud. Cars, men, horses, and broken walls were plastered with it. Casual laborers stood in the midst of it, idly scooping it up in their shovels, and throwing it where it would run back again. That night we spent in a tent hospital in Cheppy, situated on the top of a slippery hill and in the midst of a muddy shell-marked field. The cots assigned to us in one of the vacant tents were so cold that we piled blankets on them. We went to bed only partially undressed, and even then were chilled to the bone. We arose and put on our overcoats, but that did not help. For hours we shivered in the frigid dampness. From neighboring tents we heard patients coughing and breathing in grunts, and from far away east of us came the continuous thumping of the guns.

By morning—it was Monday, November 11—we had had about three hours of sleep. For penetrating cold, "Iceland's greasy mountains" were not to be compared to a sloppy, slippery hilltop in eastern France in November. When we entered the dining tent in the gray fog of early morning, we saw one of the nurses, heavily bundled up, sitting beside a wholly inadequate little stove. She remarked, in soft southern speech, "Ah think wah is the most dreatful thing that can happen. It makes everybody so *mis'able.*" That was our opinion, too.

In a big French touring car we set out with the intention of passing through Rheims and reaching Paris by nightfall. We drove through utterly desolate, ruined towns with American troops and motor trucks and horses standing in the midst of the ruins. At Sommerance, about noon, we asked a traffic officer, mired in the mud at a crossroad, whether he had any news, "Yes, the war ended at eleven o'clock." The war, the Great War, was over! The incredible had happened! I felt dazed and bewildered, in a strange world of desolation, "mis'ry," and shattered homes—and in the fog and mud that seemed a proper setting for the hideousness of it all. Could it be possible that light might break and the world be gay and joyous again? What might the future hold for us? The first shock of the news brought relief, rather than exuberance, and then a sense of wonderment as to how events might move.

A breakdown of the car and bad roads retarded our progress so that by nightfall we were able to get only as far as Épernay. Although there was joyous celebration in the city or perhaps because there was joyous celebration, all the hotels were closed. Then we learned the practical value of internationalism in science. A French medical officer we chanced to meet told us that we might find accommodations in the local hospital. There we went. The doctors and nurses were at dinner, celebrating the victory. We introduced ourselves. The doctors knew of the discovery of the bacillus of dysentery by Flexner; they were aware of Lambert's services through the American Red Cross; and one of them happened to ask if I was the Cannon who had made "classic" studies on the stomach. Thus we were properly identified, and were warmly welcomed to participate in the celebration. We sat at the doctors' table, rejoicing with them in their happiness after the long, long struggle. Speeches were exchanged, toasts were drunk, and in spite of our failure to reach Paris we thought the day well ended.

The next afternoon we were approaching Paris. From Châ-teau-Thierry onward we entered a region not damaged by the war. Flags were flying everywhere; at every village and town we were greeted by shouts and cheers; men waved their hands or saluted, children cried *"les américains."* It was a gay and jubilant journey. As we were entering Paris, the crowds grew more and more dense and the enthusiasm more boundless. We were outfitted for a reception. Our driver was grimy, our car was plastered with mud; it was evident that we were just in from the front. The people shouted their welcome; boys jumped on our running boards, waving flags in our faces; a girl made an attempt to snatch a tricolored rosette from my over-coat, and when she failed, the onlookers burst into laughter; sedate men lifted their hats to us.

Dr. Lambert returned to his home while Dr. Flexner and I dined together at one of the restaurants. About eight o'clock we went out to the streets. On crossing the Place de la Con-corde we came to the statue of Strasbourg, among those of her sister cities, now covered with the French Tricolor and with garlands of flowers. At last the family circle would again be complete. We jostled our way up the Rue Royale to the Boule-vard des Italiens. There the crowd was prodigious. Lines of people, arm in arm, swept by singing and shouting. Some Amer-ican soldiers, grinding out hideous squawks on klaxons in rhythmic time, had a great company following after them.

The crowd the previous evening, so it was reported, had been more sedate and more deeply impressed with the solemn joy of peace. It would have been wonderful to have seen the streets that night, too.

What an extraordinary world was being disclosed! Republics were springing up in place of tyrannies; kings were slipping away to escape disaster; dynasties, centuries old, were abolished in a few hours. As Lloyd George remarked, "Emperors, kings and crowns are falling like withered leaves before the gale." I wondered what it all meant and where the free spirit might lead.

By good fortune experiences in researches on shock during World War I could be put to use in World War II. In May, 1940, when there was fear that the United States might again be forced into a conflict, I was asked to become chairman of a Committee on Shock and Transfusions of the National Research Council. I had not given much attention to shock problems since 1923, when in a book entitled *Traumatic Shock,* I summarized the researches of World War I. Here was a call to service, however, which could not be denied. Through subsequent years of the global conflict I acted in the capacity assigned to me.

As previously noted, the studies on shock conducted in World War I had revealed that the condition was due primarily to a reduction of the volume of circulating blood. It was of urgent importance, therefore, to provide a means of increasing the volume as soon as possible, before damage could result from the reduced efficiency of the circulation. A primary method for bringing about improvement consists in augmenting the volume by infusing into a vein a somewhat gummy or colloidal solution. The solution does not, of course, increase the number of red corpuscles which carry to the tissues the constantly needed oxygen, but it puts to greater use the corpuscles which remain, by restoring the circulation to a more nearly normal state. Recent studies had shown that the fluid part of the blood, the plasma, which is easily separated from the corpuscles and which naturally is an innocuous fluid, could be used for that purpose. If preserved in a fluid state it may become contaminated with bacteria; and it is a good culture medium for them. If dried, however, this danger is avoided. With the help of Max Strumia of the Bryn Mawr Hospital, the Committee defined safe methods of drying plasma for the use of the armed forces. The procurement of blood from which the plasma could be processed was too elaborate an undertaking for the Committee and was assigned to the American Red Cross and through it to the highly efficient direction of G. Canby Robinson. The story of the extensive donation of blood by American citizens for their wounded fellows and the reports of the value of plasma in saving human lives are too well known to be recounted here.

Another important action of the Committee was the enlisting of a colleague at the Harvard Medical School, Edwin J. Cohn, the physical chemist, in the enterprise of analyzing the constituents of the plasma. He and his collaborators began their studies in the summer of 1940 and soon succeeded in making a preparation of the albumin of the plasma, the most important constituent as a blood substitute, that could be sealed and preserved in concentrated state in glass containers. Since it occupied less space than was required by the outfit for dried plasma, it was especially valuable for naval ships where space is at a premium. Ultimately, the other constituents of the plasma that were isolated may prove to be even more important than the albumin.

In addition to the foregoing activities the Committee directed researches on the nature of shock itself. These resulted in a discrimination of different types of shock—due to hemorrhage, burns, and infection—all accompanied by reduced blood volume and all requiring treatment as soon as possible after receipt of the injury. When there has been loss of blood the ideal replacement is, of course, blood itself. As mentioned above, however, plasma and albumin can definitely improve the circulation. Since they can be used in forward areas or in the midst of battle, when the transfusion of blood is difficult if not impossible, they offer an admirable substitute. At a later stage of the treatment of the wounded whole blood may be required.

And so the concern with war and its surgical problems has proved to be a chapter in my experience offering me an opportunity to engage for a time directly in practical affairs. In a career spent mainly in the excitements of research within academic bounds it has been, like them, a series of adventures.

# CHAPTER XIII

# POSSIBILITIES OF CO-OPERATIVE RESEARCH

THE ADVANTAGES of co-operative research I learned during World War I while serving as an intermediary for groups of investigators in the United States and England and again, later, during World War II in the Committee on Shock and Transfusions of the National Research Council. Since the organization of the co-operative enterprise was more thorough in the second experience, I shall limit my description to its workings. The Committee, through the acquaintance which its members had with the abilities of investigators in different parts of the country, invited engagement in researches on various unsettled aspects of the shock problem. At a conference of these prospective collaborators, the questions to be answered were discussed and outlined and the need for obtaining answers as promptly as possible was emphasized. Thus, whenever any one of the members of the group discovered something new, it could be promptly tested for its validity and appraised by other members. Moreover, results obtained in laboratory experiments could be applied at once to needs in the clinic and thereby the values in human cases could be examined and put to use in the care of wounded men. Occasional gatherings of all the investigators working on problems of shock allowed summaries of progress to be presented and points in which there was variance of testimony to be critically judged. Such gatherings commonly resulted in bringing forth features of the prob‚ lems which needed particular attention. Special experiments were then assigned to individuals whose methods could best be utilized for obtaining further light on those features.

A real satisfaction was experienced in such co-operative efforts as engaged the abilities of the shock teams in World War I. The members of the team were united in a spirit of mutual understanding and in a sense of devotion to a common cause—bringing succor to the wounded and saving life. Questions of priority of discovery usually did not arise, or if they did, they were settled by the dating of the reports. It was highly gratifying to note that progress was being achieved and that this progress was important in the war.

The war need made the co-operation possible. With a desire to participate in that effort investigators turned aside from their individual concerns and devoted themselves wholeheartedly to the work on shock. That they could be induced to follow a similar course in times of peace is highly questionable. When I returned from France in 1919, I was so much impressed by the advantages of co-operative research that I called a meeting of investigators in Boston who, I thought, might be interested in collaborating on problems related to the functions and disturbances of the thyroid gland. I had earnest hope that new insight in this obscure realm might be more rapidly obtained if we worked together. My attempt, however, was futile because no common incentive prevailed to modify the strong individual absorption of the members of the group in their personal investigations.

One of the most striking characteristics of an expert investigator is his strong individualism. He has his own personal curiosities, his own plans for work, and his own ways and methods for carrying out his plans. It is difficult for him to engage with other experts as a member of a team. New ideas for research come to mind in the course of his investigation that enticingly lead him away to fresh fields for discovery. He wishes to follow the prospects he foresees, unchecked by obligations to associates. He acts thus not because he fails to respect or appreciate highly what others are doing but because he is satisfying an eager personal interest. What proves attractive to him, furthermore, may not prove attractive to others. Indeed, it may be difficult for him to justify to others the course he intends to pursue.

It is commonly said that when an investigator follows his own enthusiasm, he is engaged in "disinterested" research. In striving to realize his surmise, to be sure, his purpose is not to render favors or to support any special doctrine. His efforts, however, are far from impersonal. They are intensely personal and an expression of his deepest concerns. Further, it should be confessed that the investigator is not engaged in devotion to science "for its own sake," to repeat a common expression. He is ready to spend strenuous days in that devotion, but with the intent of securing new knowledge and new insight for his own inner satisfaction. The "pure" science thus obtained, he is deeply convinced, will have ultimate if not immediate value beyond satisfying his curiosity.

There are innumerable examples of practical results which have flowed from the deep-delving interest of the investigator when primarily he has been gratifying his personal inquisitiveness. Röntgen was studying the effects of the discharge of electricity through attenuated gases when he discovered the rays which bear his name. He had no anticipation that these rays would prove of inestimable value in revealing the functions and disorders of internal organs, locating in the body foreign objects such as bullets or bits of shrapnel, showing the position of broken bones, and disclosing the character of crystalline structure. Similarly when Perkin made his first observations on aniline dyes he was not in the least aware of their possible use in industry, in the discrimination of different types of bacteria, in the staining of microscopic sections of tissues, in the development of medicinal agents, in the diagnosis of disease, and in the manufacture of explosives. Doubtless much that is highly valuable for human welfare can be discovered by attention to problems which are presented by definite human needs. But obviously it would be folly to limit research to what is called "applied" science. The possibilities of relieving man's estate by permitting the investigator to satisfy his "wanting to know" are too evident to warrant any such limitation.

The arguments against the planning of research are based mainly on the dangers which might arise if the unique foresight and personal drive of the investigator, whose eagerness for discovery leads him deeper and deeper into the elucidation of hidden meanings, should be neglected or suppressed. Attempts to organize research and to control its direction by governmental agents or by social theory and compulsion are fraught with such dangers. In my opinion, as I have already testified, it would be deplorable if scientific activities should become wholly dependent on governmental subvention and on a scramble for funds in competition with hosts of other demands on the public treasury. Particularly the pursuit of pure research might be seriously imperiled; legislators, unacquainted with the ways in which benefits have been obtained by applying investigative skill, might be duly impressed with plans for solving problems of practical import but they might refuse the assignment of funds for fundamental investigations which are often much more rewarding.

In expressing some apprehension of hazards to research on problems of theory if governmental control should prevail exclusively, I do not wish to imply any belittlement of the admirable aid which the national and various state governments in the United States have given toward the application of scientific methods to such problems as those of agriculture, geology, and meteorology. Nor would I fail to express high regard for the marvelous contributions to human comfort and convenience which have resulted from researches in laboratories maintained by great industrial organizations. As a rule, however, the scientific activities in these establishments are directed toward immediately practical ends. There is, to be sure, no real conflict of interests between pure and applied science, but the values of applied science are immediately obvious and are therefore likely to gain prompt and generous support. The danger lies in a consequent neglect of possibly extensive illumination gained by seeking answers to theoretical questions.

The astonishingly rapid progress in the accumulation of knowledge in many directions when there is generous financing of scientific efforts has been demonstrated by governmental subvention during World War II. In these circumstances, however, the government has provided the money required by the investigators but has left them to exercise their talents within the ranges where their insight and abilities have proved most effective. Furthermore, a group of eminent scientists, acquainted with the diverse methods of scientific inquiry, have determined where and how the funds could be best allocated in order to secure the desired results. The success of this mode of accelerating the process of advancing knowledge raises the question whether, in times of peace, there might not be similar definite advantage in co-operative research which could be promoted, possibly by governmental support, under control of a strictly scientific organization.

A possibility of co-operation in research, capable of offering many of the advantages which have been disclosed when investigators have worked together on questions presented by war, is seen when a fund of considerable magnitude is assigned for studies on a specific set of problems. The National Research Council, an organization intimately associated with the National Academy of Sciences in Washington, is an agency which receives such funds and provides groups of scientific men to attend to their effective distribution. For nearly a quarter of a century I have been a member of one of the groups, the Committee for Research in Problems of Sex; and for about a third of that time I have been chairman of another group, the Committee for Research in Endocrinology.

Experience on these two committees has demonstrated that there can be a form of investigative activity which preserves the

benefits of co-operation, avoids the chances of governmental interference, and permits investigators to devote their energies
to their special interests. At the time the Sex Research Committee began its administration, in 1921, the problems con-
fronting it, though of great social importance, were largely
taboo. The Committee let it be generally known that a fund
existed for the support of investigations in this neglected field,
and invited applications for grants. From the beginning, therefore—and the same may be said for the Committee on Endocrinology—the applications have come only from persons already interested and active in the general field. No compulsion
has been exercised, no control has been imposed, and only opportunity for progress has been offered. During the many years
of its existence the Committee for Research in Problems of Sex
has dispensed more than a million dollars. No country in the
world has even approached the United States in its contributions to the biological and social understanding of questions
concerned with reproductive functions and their control. Occasional conferences of the responsible investigators, who have
profited by the grants-in-aid assigned to them, have yielded the
same benefits as were manifest in the conferences of the group
working on shock problems. There has been mutual stimulation due to discussion of methods and results and a promotion
of acquaintance and understanding among the participants
which have resulted in friendly exchange of ideas and in approval of the collaborative enterprise. One consequence of
this collaboration is a monumental volume entitled *Sex and Internal Secretions* (1939). In twenty-four chapters written by
members of the research group, it records the advances in
knowledge of the biology of sex that have been made in a relatively short time because a generous assignment of funds has
allowed investigators to push forward effectively in their own
programs.

There are obvious opportunities for a man of wealth to promote inquiries into any field in which he happens to be interested. During the past third of a century the life expectancy in

the United States has risen from about forty-five to more than sixty years. Conservative estimates indicate that in the not very distant future the age distribution of the inhabitants of our country will be approximately: 30 per cent below twenty years of age, 50 per cent between twenty and sixty, and 20 per cent over sixty. More than twenty-five millions in the seventh decade or beyond! Whether these projected figures prove exact or not, it is certain that the numbers of elderly persons in our population will greatly increase. The medical and social problems of old age have been sadly neglected. It has been said that young investigators are not attracted by problems of old people and that when investigators themselves become old, they no longer have the energy or the freedom to study old age themselves. I cite these considerations in order to show how co-operative studies can be advanced. A request to the National Research Council for an appraisal of the possibilities of investigating a general topic such as old age, for example, or any particular aspect of old age results in the appointment of a committee of experts which would in time give their opinion. If their testimony should result in the granting of a subvention for a considerable number of years by the interested party or parties, the National Research Council would then ask the committee of experts, or possibly some modification of that committee, to serve as an administrative agency in dispensing the available money to reliable investigators already engaging in pertinent research or attracted into such activity by knowing that their efforts would be assisted.

Clearly a governmental agency could utilize the long experience, the knowledge and the skill of the National Research Council in a similar manner for the investigation of any problem in which it was concerned.

Ample research funds, given for specific purposes and under control of competent scientists free from political pressure, provide conditions which in many respects favor the most extensive and the most rapid progress in science. The individual interests of the participating investigators are given free scope, for they are permitted to go their own way. The values of co-operation are preserved as the investigators, who are interested in a given field, labor in that field and are at times brought together for comparison and discussion of their experiences. Planning, in the sense of directing work on important problems, is unnecessary; the assignment of funds does that. The only defect in the general scheme that I can see is possible failure to assist some types of investigation which are important but which do not attract support.

# CHAPTER XIV

# BEING A CITIZEN

THE SCIENTIFIC investigator is commonly thought of as an academic recluse. Many investigators do, to be sure, lead lives which are largely dissociated from public service. This does not mean, of course, that their labors fail to bring advantage to the general population. Indeed, the lone investigator, just because he is single-minded, may produce results which are of incalculable value in benefiting mankind. Faraday, for example, though sometimes leading in the devotions of a small religious sect to which he adhered, "took little part in social movements and went little into society." It must be admitted that *time,* the irreplaceable necessity for scientific achievement, may be largely lost in activities irrelevant to scientific concern. Nevertheless, the scientist is also a citizen and may feel a compulsion to engage in services which he as a citizen has opportunities to perform. And if *freedom,* essential for productive scholarship, is threatened, the call to engage in defense of it may be imperative.

When I was a medical student I heard a talk by the late William T. Sedgwick, in which he advised his listeners first to establish themselves in their professional careers, perhaps by the time they reached forty years of age, and thereafter to spend weekly a certain amount of time in attention to public affairs. This talk made a deep impression. Not until I was nearly forty years old did the chance come for me to follow Professor Sedgwick's suggestion. In 1908 I was chairman of the Section on Physiology and Pathology of the American Medical Association. For more than a decade the antivivisectionists had striven to restrict freedom of medical research in Massachusetts, and during about the same period they had made similar efforts in Pennsylvania. It seemed to me pertinent to discuss the aims of the antivivisectionists, their misconceptions, the methods they employed to realize their objectives, and the danger which might ensue to the population at large, should they be successful. This I did in my chairman's address.

The fundamental mischief of the antivivisectionists in agitating against medical research is, as I have already pointed out, their presentation of a misleading issue. They deny that any utility has come from animal experimentation, they describe the experiments as horrible torturing of dumb brutes, and then they ask if this futile cruelty shall be permitted to go on. If this were the whole and veracious story, few would hesitate on which side to stand. Every decent man and woman is opposed to cruelty; every decent human being winces at the thought of inflicted pain. But that is not the whole story. Nor is it veracious. It would be as fair to display a picture of Dr. Grenfell, fighting his faithful dogs and stabbing them to death, labeled "Is this the way to treat your pets?" as it is to represent animal experimentation without its motives and without its triumphs. Grenfell, in his struggle on the frigid ice pan, stabbed his dogs in order to save his own life, and every person with common sense commends the bravery, the resourcefulness, and the proper sense of values of that missionary hero. Any worthy man who sees straight would try to do what Grenfell did, if he were cornered and had to sacrifice his own life or that of lower animals.

This is precisely the issue which the investigators see. Furthermore, they are aware of overwhelming evidence that by the experimental use of some animals the chances for life and health of all mankind, and of myriads of lower animals as well, have been enormously amplified. All that the uninstructed need do is to read what is known regarding the direct and practical relation of animal experiments to the effective treatment of diphtheria and tetanus, to meningitis, rabies, and smallpox, to dysentery, cholera and typhoid fever, to bubonic plague, tuberculosis and syphilis, to the disturbances of internal secretions, to diabetes and pernicious anemia, to the action of drugs, to the advancement of surgical technique, to childbirth, to hygiene and preventive medicine—in order to learn of the incomparable service which animals in the laboratories have rendered for their fellow creatures. Just because they have rendered such service, we turn to them for succor as we contemplate the still unconquered afflictions of men and women and children whose sufferings extend to everyone bound to them by the strong ties of love and sympathy. Of the animal used for solving the mystery of disease William James wrote, with illuminating insight, "If his poor benighted mind could only be made to catch a glimpse of the human intentions, all that is heroic in him would religiously acquiesce."

Such points as these I emphasized in my address. In the audience was the eminent pathologist, William H. Welch, who, at a famous hearing before a Congressional Committee in Washington in 1900, had proved himself a vigorous defender of freedom of medical investigation. Whether in consequence of the address I do not know, but almost immediately thereafter the Association appointed a Committee for the Protection of Medical Research, and asked me to be chairman. My associates on the Committee were a remarkable group of men: Joseph Capps, professor of medicine in the University of Chicago; Reid Hunt, the well-known pharmacologist of the United States Public Health Service; David L. Edsall, professor of pediatrics at the University of Pennsylvania and later dean of the Harvard Medical School; Simon Flexner, director of the Rockefeller Institute; and Harvey Cushing, the brain surgeon, who for many years was my colleague and close friend.

This group, with few changes, worked together for seventeen years. Our first task was to examine the conditions under which experimental medicine was being conducted in the United States. Inquiry revealed that in a number of laboratories there had been posted for many years regulations defining the humane treatment of animals used for experimental purposes. We collected these scattered regulations and generalized them so that they would be applicable throughout the country. They provided for caution in using stray cats and dogs by arranging a delay before their use, at least as long as that which was customary in the local pound; they stipulated the kind of care in the housing and feeding of the animals; they demanded use of anesthesia when the operative procedure involved more discomfort than that of giving the anesthetic; and they provided for putting the animals to death before recovery from the anesthetic unless the director of the laboratory authorized recovery for the purposes of the experiment. These regulations were printed on a large display card. They were adopted by corporate action of medical faculties and medical research institutes throughout the United States, and the cards were prominently posted in laboratory rooms wherever experimental work was being carried on. The members of the Committee were convinced that these regulations were chiefly valuable in assuring the interested public that the procedures in animal experimentation are conducted in a humane manner.

As intimated above, antivivisection literature reveals the prevalence of two general ideas. First, there is the charge that animals are experimented on with utter disregard for avoidance of inflicting pain; indeed, many of the claims of cruelty in medical research would give the uninstructed reader the impression that the experimenters are hideous, immoral monsters. This is a view which might be corrected by actual visits to the laboratories. In 1923, the Committee was so thoroughly convinced that the methods of animal experimentation were routinely above reproach in the judgment of reasonable persons that it secured adherence from the deans of medical schools throughout the land to what was called the "open-door policy." This policy provided that any interested member of a humane society might visit the laboratories at any time. The only qualification imposed in some instances was that the visitor must previously have seen an operation on a human being. It is an

instructive fact that very few representatives of humane societies have taken advantage of this opportunity.

The Committee also met the second charge of the antivivisectionists—that animal experimentation is both misleading and
useless. Even when the Committee was established, more than
a third of a century ago, the charge had little force. Antiseptic
surgery and aseptic surgery had become recognized as a consequence of experiments on lower animals, the death rate from
diphtheria and tuberculosis had markedly dropped (in both
diseases the result of animal experimentation), and other
similar achievements could be pointed to with satisfaction.
Nevertheless, there was no widespread understanding of the
importance of the experimental method for the advancement
of medical knowledge. In order to diffuse the evidence for that
fact, well-known experts in various fields were invited to prepare articles on the vital significance of animal experiments for
progress in practical medicine and surgery—articles on diphtheria, tuberculosis, child-bed fever, venereal disease, disorders
of the heart and blood vessels, surgical technique, veterinary
medicine, tropical disease, and other subjects. These authoritative expositions were published in the *Journal of the American
Medical Association* and later reprinted as pamphlets. They
had wide distribution and doubtless did much to acquaint both
the profession and the public with the essential value of laboratory experimentation for the welfare of human beings and
the welfare of lower animals also. In the last three decades the
demonstration of these values has become so familiar to the
public that the antivivisectionists' charge of uselessness is reduced to absurdity. Indeed, now that hundreds of thousands
of Americans contribute to a fund, part of which is used to
carry on animal experiments in order to secure insight into the
nature of infantile paralysis, the antivivisectionists are having
more and more difficulty in obtaining support for their harmful agitation.

In England where, since 1876, there has been restrictive legislation against the use of animals for medical and biological

research, the antivivisection societies were not reduced in number thereby but in fact increased, until there were a dozen or more. Restrictive legislation is not sufficient for them; it is the camel's head inside the tent. The ultimate purpose of the extremist is not to restrict but to abolish the practice. It is immoral, they declare, to take the lives of lower animals as they are taken in the laboratories, even though mankind is benefited thereby—hence no compromise. We have been warned against following England's example and strongly advised against allowing even the initial steps of restrictive legislation. The Committee for the Protection of Medical Research has fought the efforts of the antivivisectionists to pass hostile bills in the legislatures of various eastern states, in Congress, and in popular referenda in Colorado and California. It is gratifying to report that thus far the antivivisectionists have not been able in the United States to interfere with medical investigators in their efforts to increase knowledge of disease and to discover effective ways of treating it. With due precautions against the infliction of pain they are still as free as the experimenters in physics and chemistry to project their explorations into the dark ranges of ignorance.

The responsibilities of citizenship may not be restricted to one's own community, state, or nation. Circumstances extended my interest in freedom to a wider scope. In 1930, while serving as exchange professor to French universities, I motored with members of my family into Spain, in order to meet former students who occupied teaching positions there. At both Barcelona and Madrid the university groups were openly talking of a republic. At Madrid, the professor of physiology and acting dean of the medical school was Juan Negrín. We had exchanged reprints of our scientific papers and were well acquainted with each other's scientific interests. At that time Dr. Negrín was deeply involved in planning and superintending the erection of impressive structures which, as the University City, he hoped to see develop into a center of culture for Spanish-speaking people throughout the world. With enthusiasm he showed me the buildings which were already in existence and the model of the complete city.

Dr. Negrín's planning for the future contrasted sharply with his strong feelings about the recent past and, indeed, about the then existing conditions in Spain. This contrast was widespread. I first encountered evidences of deep resentment when I asked one of my former students about the dictator, Primo de Rivera, whose regime had ended only a few months previously. I have never known a simple inquiry to rouse so manifest a display of intense emotion. He turned pale, became greatly agitated, and answered me in a voice which quavered with pent feeling. Such was the effect of despotic government on a liberty-loving citizen. The behavior of the dictator reflected on the king. While we were in Madrid, Dr. Negrín escorted us one day to the Escorial, that forbidding granite structure, part monastery, part palace and part mausoleum, in which lie the bodies of rulers of Spain since the middle of the sixteenth century. As we stood in the crypt, surrounded by the sepulchers of the departed kings and emperors, he quietly turned to us and with grim satisfaction drew our attention to the fact that there was provision for only one more king. The situation in Spain at that time was such that I wrote to a friend in the United States urging him to watch Spain for momentous developments. Almost exactly a year later the municipal elections caused the king to take a hint and precipitately leave the country.

In 1935, at an International Physiological Congress, I met Dr. Negrín again. Meanwhile he had accepted a position in the government. He did this, so he told me, because he was convinced that he could help his country more in public service than in teaching and carrrying on investigations in the medical school. I could understand his attitude, for I knew that Spain had undergone turbulent experiences since 1931. Early in 1936, only a few months after our meeting, the elections occurred which brought into power the liberal element of the Spanish population and roused in the conservative element deep apprehension. The story since that time is well known. Franco, with the open support of the troops of Hitler and Mussolini, with plentiful equipment in tanks, heavy guns, and armed airplanes supplied by those aggressive dictators, attacked the unprepared, ill-equipped, and much depleted army of the Republic. Apologists for Franco declared that he was saving Christianity in Spain; it is well to recognize that he did so by importing Mohammedan Moors. As was their custom, he and his fascist helpers raised the cry that they were fighting the spread of Bolshevism. There were, indeed, Russian technicians in the Republican service but no Russian troops. Furthermore, evidence of communist control of the government was minimal. The election of February, 1936, had returned only sixteen communists out of 473 members of the Cortes. At that time there were no communists in the government and later there were only two in the cabinet of nine. In a letter from Dr. Negrín, written to me after he became premier of the Republic, he declared that he could not understand the misleading charge of communist control of Spain except as a conspiracy on the part of Hitler and Mussolini to prejudice world opinion against the legitimate Spanish government. How true this judgment was is indicated by shouts of the same slogan by these tyrannical dictators in attempting later to secure support for the savage actions of their own armies.

There was little that groups of citizens could do to aid the Spanish Republic in its struggle for liberty. The national governments of England and France, on the plea of nonintervention, refused to the legitimate Spanish government the right, recognized in international law, to purchase arms for its own defense; and the government of the United States followed their example. The Neutrality Committee in London was, in effect, supporting Franco and his ruthless fascist collaborators. In the circumstances the only action friends of the Spanish Republic could take was that of providing medical and surgical supplies, clothing, and food. For more than two years I served as national chairman of the Medical Bureau to Aid Spanish

Democracy. During that time we sent to Spain medical personnel and surgical instruments, hospital equipment and ambulances, amounting in value to more than a million dollars. Naturally enough I was charged with being a Bolshevik, a supporter of communism, an enemy of the Roman Catholic church, and in general a Red, with all the dark insinuations then implied in that term. Because of the many letters which had to be written, the many conferences and committee meetings which had to be attended, and because of the gatherings which had to be addressed in Philadelphia, Detroit, and elsewhere, and also because of the political controversy, this whole experience was very time-consuming. I do not regret, however, having followed the course I have just outlined; I only regret that our efforts were not effective in helping at last to achieve the common degrees of freedom among a people long held in ignorance and economic repression.

After being subjected to much hostile criticism and spending much time in doing what I could for the Spanish Loyalists, I confess to having felt a sense of satisfaction as I read the testimony of Sumner Welles in his *Time for Decision*. In 1944, eight years after the start of the war in Spain, he admitted that many Americans were beginning to realize more accurately that the real question raised by fascist and nazi policy toward that country was whether a popular government, elected by the people and representing democratic ideals and aspirations, should be overthrown with impunity, not by revolution inside Spain but by the armed forces of Hitler and Mussolini. "In the long history of the foreign policy of the Roosevelt administration," he concludes, "there has been, I think, no more cardinal error than the policy adopted during the civil war in Spain."

Experience in China as a visiting professor at the Peking Union Medical School, in 1935, revealed to me a situation which resembled that in Spain in 1930. The returned western students were earnestly desirous of bringing to their native land conditions they had observed while studying abroad. It seemed to me that a fresh ferment was at work in China's ancient civilization and that she was on the verge of an extraordinary new development which would lead to greatly increased strength. All that the liberal elements asked for in order to make China independent of foreign invasion was a decade of peace in which to bring about the contemplated changes. Obviously Japan beheld the dangers resident in such delay. Already the Japanese troops stationed at Peking were manifesting an arrogance and effrontery in their behavior toward Chinese civilians that made my blood boil. The poor Chinese, almost helpless peace-lovers, could do nothing to prevent such malicious and tyrannical actions of the little brown men. As my wife and I were leaving China early in June, 1935, for Mukden and for cities in Korea, trainloads of Japanese soldiers passed us on their way to the ancient capital. The oppressive conduct of the Japanese grew worse and worse as the months passed thereafter, until in June, 1937, they started the war which finally brought our country into the global conflict as China's ally. It is a satisfaction to me that before the United States became a military supporter of the Chinese cause, I was privileged to help in the services performed by the American Bureau for Medical Aid to China and by the United China Relief.

One other opportunity for possible usefulness outside the laboratory appeared when there was organized an American-Soviet Medical Society. I had counted Pavlov as one of my friends, and I had other scientific friends and acquaintances in Leningrad and Moscow. They were as kind, considerate and generous as any I have known. The vast social effort in which they were engaged was different from that in which I placed my trust, but it was directed toward bettering the lives of their fellow citizens. Also their country and mine were striving together in a supreme effort to end Hitler's mad slaughter of innocent people and ruthless destruction of precious human values. The outcome of that struggle would leave us both powerful nations, capable of exerting incalculably great influence in favoring peaceful pursuits. It seemed to me, therefore, highly important that there should be good understanding and good will between the people of the United States and the people of the Soviet Union. So when the presidency of the American-Soviet Medical Society was offered to me, I accepted it. This I did, not with any illusion that a small society would have, directly, great influence. The fact should be recognized, however, that the medical profession is the most widespread fraternity in the world. Doctors are bound together by their common desire and common function of mitigating human distress. A small association of doctors, therefore, may have an extensive influence because of membership in the big fraternity. Admittedly, this is an experiment. Since I have been an experimenter throughout my professional career, I do not hesitate to try fair possibilities.

A close relation exists between democracy and science. Modern democracy developed with industries—as scientific research and experimenting and inventing produced multitudes of contrivances, as the contrivances brought people together in populous cities and required varieties of skill and intelligence in work on technical procedures. With increasing density of population, points of contact between individuals and groups multiplied and opportunities for concerted thinking and action for common interests greatly increased. The natural results were free popular education, public hospitals, protection of community health, and numerous other well-known consequences of the democratic process.

A close relation exists also between liberty and democracy. One of the finest definitions of democracy was given by a scientific investigator, Pasteur, when he said that it is "the form of government in which everyone is free to do his best for the public welfare." The words express recognition of the liberty of the individual and they imply recognition of the essential organic relations of the individual to the common body politic. What he does for public welfare has values for all members of the social order, himself included. In contrast, government by despotic tyrants, as recent events have glaringly illustrated, can crush individual liberty and can force violent actions which both destroy the possibilities of national happiness and prosperity and bring appalling disasters on all the world.

No enlightened observer would admit that the democratic ideal and its attendant freedom have been nearly achieved, or that what has been achieved is fixed and secure. The existence of unwarrantably privileged classes, of hopeless economic groups, and of powerful selfish interests which press heavily for specially favorable legislation, shows that much remains to be done. Democracy, in truth, is vulnerable. Ralph Barton Perry cites three reasons why its persistence cannot be taken for granted: (1) democracy has not yet been attained; (2) its attainment requires moral effort; and (3) what has been attained has to be vigilantly protected. "Like all living things it must grow, it must be kept alive, and it must be guarded." In this world, now little, what happens far away may have dire endings at home, for peoples are more and more closely bound together in a single fate.

All these considerations have a direct bearing on the role of the scientific investigator as a citizen. The unchecked pursuit of his most cherished desires depends immediately on the liberty which a democratic government most reliably provides. He does well, therefore, to watch over it and, if necessary, to go forth from his "serene attachment to the processes of inquiry and understanding" to battle for its security.

I am grateful that fortunate conditions gave me opportunities to test democratic methods by opposing the efforts of antivivisectionists at destroying freedom of medical investigation; to attempt aiding republican forces in Spain and in China as they struggled against oppressors; and to promote deeper sympathy and understanding between the Americans and the Russians as they look forward to a better world.

# CHAPTER XV

# MAKING SCIENCE UNDERSTANDABLE

WHETHER a scientific investigator should at any time engage in attempting popular education by simplifying accounts of what he has done, in order that they may be understood by the laity, is a matter for individual judgment. There are good precedents both for popularizing and for refusing to popularize. Huxley and Tyndall, for example, by publishing articles of general interest, did much during the last century to draw attention to the scientific fields they cultivated.

My feeling about public education is based upon a conviction that it is important for science to be understood in a democracy. Popular enlightenment is essential. Support for scientific enterprise comes from private individuals or industrial organizations or from such public interest as will lead to the voting of subventions by legislative bodies. In the United States there is fortunately among the citizens an increasing comprehension of the motives and methods as well as of the results of scientific discovery. With the belief that there is definite value in promoting such comprehension, I have taken time to express in popular form accounts of various groups of investigations which have been carried on by me and my collaborators. Thus the researches on the effects of emotional excitement were presented in a manner which could be generally understood in *Bodily Changes in Pain, Hunger, Fear and Rage,* and the studies concerned with the maintenance of steady states in the organism were described in *The Wisdom of the Body.* Another volume, *Digestion and Health,* was written with the same intent. It has seemed to me preferable for the investigator, himself, to interpret his labors to the general public rather than running the risk of misinterpretation by the ill-informed.

The attitude I have taken is not common among investigators. Some feel that they are incapable of writing in a style suited to the layman; others despise efforts at popularizing science and may even go to the extreme of declaring that such efforts are prostituting science by an appeal to the mob. As I have said in the foregoing chapter, however, the investigator is bound to recognize that he is also a citizen. The argument may be urged that because knowledge of science is fundamental to intelligent citizenship and therefore desirable, he should regard the diffusion of that knowledge as a public duty. In England there appears to have been a much earlier recognition of the importance of popular scientific instruction than in the United States. The Royal Institution, for example, has been, since its foundation in 1799, a place where research of the highest order has been conducted and where also popular lectures and demonstrations have been given by the eminent men who have served as its directors, from Sir Humphry Davy through Faraday, Dewar, Bragg, and others to the present director, Sir Henry H. Dale.

In the United States there has long been a spreading of scientific information through the *Popular Science Monthly* (later the *Scientific Monthly*) and through *Science,* which are now distributed, one or the other, to more than 25,000 members of the American Association for the Advancement of Science, as well as to public libraries throughout the country. The articles in both these publications are in the main written by expert investigators, who tell about their special interests. Furthermore, in recent years specialized scientific writers have been trained who prepare "science columns" for newspapers and interpret the contributions presented at scientific meetings. The members of the Science Writers Association take pride in careful, accurate, and respectful reporting. The chief publication representative of this development is the weekly *Science News*

*Letter,* which goes extensively to the public press and to interested individuals, professional and lay.

In addition to magazines and other periodicals designed to instruct the public, there has been also in the United States use of radiobroadcasting and moving pictures. Scientific investigators as well as laymen have engaged in these modes of enlightenment. That there is still much to be done to spread scientific learning cannot be too strongly emphasized.

When an investigator is engaged in studies which are likely to prove useful or entertaining to the general reader, news of it may spread and reach the ears of representatives of the public press. In such circumstances visits from reporters and telephone calls from newspaper offices are inevitable. It has been my practice strictly to deny interviews concerning work which is in progress. Inquirers have been informed that in due season the results of the investigation will be published in a scientific periodical and that then the information will be available to all interested parties. Before the professional science writers began to serve newspaper syndicates, individual reporters, more enterprising than intelligent and often more imaginative than veracious, described as best they could the latest discoveries. Incidents which occurred in my experience illustrate the resultant appeal to sensationalism rather than to sensible understanding.

About thirty years ago I reported to the American Physiological Society that my collaborators and I had found that a strong emotion, such as rage, is attended by an increase of sugar in the blood. At that time the ordinary newspapermen did not risk the dreariness of attempting to understand the technical proceedings of a scientific meeting. On this particular occasion there was, however, unknown to me, a reporter in the audience. The next morning a release from the Associated Press announced the astounding information that "man is sweetest when angry." The dailies from Maine to California spread the glad tidings, so that all might know.

The humor of that news item was not neglected. The old periodical, *Life,* pictured a man standing at the far end of a disordered room, ready to fling a lamp angrily to the floor, as his fond wife remarked to her daughter, "Isn't he sweet!" In another publication a writer painstakingly calculated that if everybody in the United States could be angry once a month and could produce thereby an ounce of sugar, the total, if collected, would be enough to bring low the sugar trust.

Occasionally an inexpert popularizer of scientific discoveries will use a word or phrase, not warranted by what he has read, that changes radically the investigator's report. Experiments on the effect of adrenaline on a muscle, which had been extremely fatigued by rapidly repeated electrical stimulation, showed that this powerful agent has the remarkable property of quickly abolishing the fatigue and restoring the muscle to its original responsiveness. Measurement of the sensitivity to stimulation proved that a small dose of adrenaline can have in a few moments as great a restorative effect as perhaps an hour or more of complete rest. When a careless reporter, perusing a scientific journal, came upon the article in which this discovery was described, he wrote an account of the procedure which was used, and he declared that it proved adrenaline to be a substitute for rest and sleep. In the article nothing about sleep had been mentioned.

The results of this surprising announcement were marvelous. Letters poured into the laboratory from all parts of the country, written by persons who could not sleep and wanted adrenaline and also by persons who felt that they slept too much and wanted it to lessen their apparent need. Cartoonists took out their pencils and gave their imagination free play. A new style of sleeping car was pictured with the passengers conversing or playing cards or reading, while the porter, carrying a carafe labeled "Adrenaline," announces, "Fo' A.M., sah! Have yuh adrenaline?" A mattress factory was displayed festooned with cobwebs because the new discovery had put it out of use.

The formation of a Science Writers Association has greatly improved the relations between scientists and the public. I feel sure that members of that Association would not make the mistake of regarding adrenaline as a substitute for sleep and I doubt whether they would broadcast the spectacular announcement that man is sweetest when angry.

The necessary "publicity" in which every scientific investigator engages when he describes, in an article published in a scientific journal, the procedures he has employed and the results he has obtained in any given research is not intended for public instruction. His readers will be scientists, trained as he has been trained and consequently familiar with the technical vocabulary he employs. He makes no effort, therefore, to have his description intelligible to the uninstructed. It is here that the interpreter of science performs his functions, whether he is the investigator who attempts to render his ideas and actions intelligible or the skillful lay writer who has learned to understand the investigator's meaning.

The chief grievance which the popularizer expresses is that the teaching of science in grade schools, high schools, and even colleges does not result in a public with a sufficient background of knowledge to allow understanding of the simplest account of new advances. This is a deplorable situation. For a hundred years scientific investigators have been transforming the civilized world. The progress of knowledge in recent times is chiefly progress in knowledge of science and the scientific method. The investigators in physics, in chemistry, and in the medical sciences have brought about conditions, within the life span of many now living, that would seem to their fathers nothing short of miraculous. And yet, in spite of the amazing transformations wrought by scientific discoveries, instruction in science is still not regarded as an essential part of a balanced education. The incongruity persists that a man may be considered highly cultivated who has no sound acquaintance with either the important facts or the procedures of the most potent factor in modern life. Just because new knowledge is constantly being discovered by investigators there should be, in the general population and among persons in responsible positions, a sufficient understanding of the basic elements of science to permit the new knowledge to be at least appreciated.

As a physiologist I am especially impressed by the common ignorance of bodily organs and their functions. It seems to me now, as it seemed to Robert Boyle nearly three hundred years ago, that it is "highly dishonorable for a Reasonable Soul to live in so Divinely built a Mansion as the Body she resides in, altogether unacquainted with the exquisite structure of it." There are still among us benighted persons who would sympathize with the member of the House of Commons who, commenting on the extravagance of the London School Board, declared: "Physiology, besides being costly and useless, is an immodest subject. When the Author of the Universe hid the liver of man out of sight He did not want frail human creatures to see how He had done it." Indeed, when my academic title was advanced to that of a full professorship, a sensitive Cambridge lady, who had learned somehow that I was working on the activities of the digestive tract, was heard to remark, "I do hope that now he will give up his disgusting researches on the stomach." I was not aware, however, of becoming more "refined" in my interests when I turned from concern with the alimentary canal to studies on the influence of emotions in the body.

If any further indications of the need for education in science were requested, they could be found in the actions of legislative bodies in the United States to prohibit the teaching of certain aspects of biology, the evolution of species. The idea that in the long run demonstrable evidence can be suppressed by a majority vote of a small group of ill-informed men is grotesque in its futility. By passing such a law they not only revealed their own ignorance; they strove to promote ignorance among their own citizens.

What are some of the general features of science which should be set forth as important for popular appreciation of what it has to offer?

First, I would urge the need for instruction in the scientific type of thinking. By this I mean a critical attitude toward authoritative statements and an insistence on evidence—evidence based on reliable observations, on cautious inference, and on accurate tests. As an example, real discipline in this sort of thinking would automatically abolish what, from the scientific point of view, is a public scandal—the display and sale of magazines on astrology and, in many newspapers throughout the United States, the printing of a column devoted to personal astrological predictions. This utter perversion of science is a symptom of the confused mental state of large numbers of our people, and is a serious indictment of our popular educational system.

"One of the only two articles that remain in my creed of life," wrote John Dewey, "is that the future of our civilization depends upon the widening spread and deepening hold of the scientific habit of mind, and that the problem of problems in our education is therefore to discover how to mature and make effective this scientific habit. Mankind thus far has been ruled by things and by words, not by thought, for until the last few moments of history, humanity has not been in possession of the conditions of secure and effective thinking. . . . If ever we are to be governed by intelligence, not by things and by words, science must have something to say about what we do, and not merely about how we may do it most easily and economically. And if this consummation is achieved, the transformation must occur through education, by bringing home to men's habitual inclination and attitude the significance of genuine knowledge and the full import of the conditions required for its attainment."

A feature of science which is not commonly understood and which could properly be included in a popularizing program is the esthetic satisfactions it provides. Variety and richness of experience are encountered in the observation of processes or in the study of objects, that can awaken deepest wonder and admiration. Albert Michelson, awarded a Nobel prize for his researches on light, has testified, "If a poet could at the same time be a physicist, he might convey to others the pleasure, the satisfaction, almost the reverence, which the subject of light inspires. The esthetic side of the subject is, I confess, by no means the least attractive to me." In physiology the beauties of adaption in the organism—the marvelous adjustments which occur in muscular effort, for example—never fail to stir my enthusiasm whenever I am called upon to tell about them.

The citizen should know also that scientists regard the processes of nature as in a flux. Even the earth itself is mobile, undergoing changes now which it has been undergoing for eons past—mountains lifted and torn down, persistent streams carrying away the land, layers of silt deposited in ocean beds, movements of glacial ice smoothing rocks in their path and bearing huge boulders on their backs to strange environs. And animal life, types of disease, forms of social organization, all are undergoing alterations. In human affairs, science and inventions based on scientific discovery have wrought. stupendous modifications in our daily living. In my lifetime I have seen the development of the telephone, the automobile, electric lighting, control of infections, radio transmission, the airplane, and other minor members of this group of gigantic transformers. To resent the effects of science, to see it "destroying all the simplicity and gentleness of life, all the beauty of the world—restoring barbarism under the mask of civilization, darkening men's minds and hardening their hearts," is to admit an inability to face realities and make adjustments—precisely the functions which distinguish man, with his superior brain, from lower animals.

A final feature of science which I may mention, which is little recognized and which should be a part of the instruction given to the public, is what may properly be called its spiritual value. This is found in the willingness to submit one's judgment to the control of facts. Or, to put it in more common terms, it is a supreme respect for the truth. As Huxley expressed it, "Science seems to me to teach in the highest and strongest manner the great truth which is embodied in the Christian conception of entire surrender to the will of God. Sit down before facts as a little child, be prepared to give up every preconceived notion, follow humbly to whatever abysses Nature leads, or you will know nothing." If this moral attitude, which inspires the scientific investigator, were commonly accepted, discrepancies, which have long prevailed and which have momentous consequences, would be resolved. I may refer, for example, to the evidence that man did not fall from a state of perfection and therefore does not require to be redeemed; instead, through a prodigious process of evolution, he has gradually risen, in spite of frequent backsliding, from the brutish state to higher and higher degrees of civilized development. In its spiritual value, therefore, established truth is accepted by the man of science though it may contradict long-accepted dogma and tradition. By liberating the human intelligence from vague fears and apprehensions and from authoritative tyranny, science takes a stand sympathetic with the humanities.

CHAPTER XVI

# FRIENDSHIPS AT HOME AND ABROAD

FRIENDSHIPS naturally develop on the basis of a community of interests. An investigator is likely, therefore, to have more professional than nonprofessional friends. The nonprofessional friends, however, add variety and enrichment of experience that are so precious as to be sought and cherished. Life in an academic community fortunately offers exceptional opportunities for the growth of intellectual intimacies between persons of widely different disciplines. It has been my good fortune to have as my two closest and dearest friends Ralph Barton Perry, the philosopher, and George W. Pierce, the physicist. For many decades we have been intimates, in our personal relations, in our adventures, and in our exchange of ideas. Thus my understanding has been broadened—by the one toward general concepts in the world of values, and by the other toward sharp discriminations in the realm of basic science.

George Pierce and Ralph Perry were members of the Wicht Club, an informal organization of young Harvard instructors that existed early in this century. The club was named from a picture in *Simplicissimus,* a little gnomelike, red-draped figure, standing in a niche at the roots of a huge tree and with inquiring eyes peering out from under its hood. It was labeled *"Das Wicht."* The Wicht Club met once a month at a Boston hotel and, in mingled seriousness and jocularity, listened to one of the members who told about recently developed phases of his academic interest. Annually, until they became too numerous, the reprints of our published papers were gathered and bound under the title "Was Wichtiges."

The scientific investigators in the club included, besides George Pierce, Gilbert N. Lewis, for many years illustrious head of the department of chemistry at the University of California; Robert M. Yerkes, the moving spirit in founding the station for primate biology at Orange Park, Florida, now named the Yerkes Laboratory; and Ernest E. Southard, neuropathologist, a whimsical, brilliant, and stimulating leader in the advancement of psychiatry. Ernest Southard's brief life and his exceptional qualities have been described in Frederick P. Gay's *The Open Mind*. He was prone to put words to uncommon uses or to employ odd and unfamiliar words. I recall his explaining a tiresome speech, to which he had listened, as being "too damned homogeneous." A big dictionary, then recently published, had a line through every page separating the usual from the unusual words. Lewis accused Southard of hitting the dictionary below the belt! The friendships established in the Wicht Club have continued through the decades, though separation in later years has interfered with the earlier intimacies.

One of my most unique friendships outside the professional range, one which I highly prized, was with Ernest Harold Baynes, the naturalist. He was a devoted lover of animals, both wild and tame. His farm in Vermont was a preserve for all sorts of creatures. Possibly his deepest delight he found in winning the confidence of wild animals. Birds would fly to him to take food from his lips. He trained a young buffalo to be driven in harness. Someone gave him a western prairie wolf which he brought up from whelphood to be a domestic animal. This particular pet he regarded as a choice companion. By chance one of his occasional visits to Boston coincided with the opening of a dog show. The fantastic idea occurred to him that it would be adventurous to enter the tractable wolf as a competitor. This he did. The animal remained on exhibition until the judges appeared. They were astounded to find the strange creature in the show and immediately gave orders that it be excluded.

The only place to which Mr. Baynes could take his pet during the few remaining days of his stay in Boston was his hotel room. Every night he put the animal on leash and went for a long walk. Late one evening, as he was sauntering along the central, parked area of Commonwealth Avenue, the wolf suddenly had a convulsion. At the very moment of the seizure a well-known playboy of one of Boston's first families happened on the scene and asked what was the trouble. Mr. Baynes quickly explained the situation.

Thereupon the young man slapped his thigh and exclaimed, "I know exactly what's needed," and rushed away to the near-by apartment of a doctor friend. He whistled up the speaking tube and roused the doctor, who wished to know what was wanted. The young man shouted excitedly, "There's a prairie wolf having a convulsion on Commonwealth Avenue and I want some whiskey for him." The doctor replied promptly, "I think you've had enough for tonight. You'd better go home and go to bed."

Because Mr. Baynes was a great lover of animals he was urged by antivivisectionists to support their cause. In a spirit of fairness he visited the laboratories of experimental medicine to learn about the treatment of animals within them. He emerged from this experience a vigorous defender of animal experimentation.

Though my nonprofessional friendships were more intimate than those which developed over my range of scientific activity, the latter were much more numerous. In 1935, while preparing an address for the International Physiological Congress at Leningrad, I calculated that the ratios of physiologists to the total population in the United States and in England were approximately the same—one to one hundred and thirty thousand. Among the relatively few and scattered physiological investigators, there develop international acquaintances, especially among those who are working in related fields. Thus during travels or on receiving visitors one may encounter colleagues previously known only through exchanged reprints and letters, which now prove to be the basis of lasting and valued friendships. These friendships may extend into many countries. It has been my good fortune to enjoy such congenial relations on a world-wide scale.

First among my friends in the progression I may mention Sir William M. Bayliss. During the winter of 1917-18, as I have already noted, I had the great privilege of working with him on a problem of shock. Dr. Bayliss was a master of scientific methods. He was always careful to set down immediately the details of an experimental procedure; and when that procedure was complicated he would record at the time the quality of the experiment—whether it was "good" or "poor," i.e., whether all went well or not. He was an extraordinarily learned man. I remember that one day Professor A. N. Cushny came in from his neighboring laboratory of pharmacology to consult, as he said, the "encyclopedia"; on asking about the structural formula of an organic compound he received from Dr. Bayliss a prompt answer, giving the formula. No other physiologist I have known was a more delightful companion or had a keener appreciation of humor than Sir William. At the time we were working together, Lady Bayliss, who was managing a community kitchen, reported how rapidly it had been possible to feed persons who resorted to it, and then commented on the meagerness of supplies. I told the family that this reminded me of the boy who was furiously painting a fence. When asked why he was wielding the brush so rapidly, he replied that he was "trying to get the job done before the paint gave out." Sir William's laughter was quick and hearty.

The mention of Bayliss naturally brings to my memory his lifelong collaborator, E. H. Starling. One afternoon during World War I, as the three of us were having tea in the laboratory, we were visited by one of my former students. He was in uniform. He sat down with us and, with excellent poise and social ease, participated in the conversation. After he had departed I explained to Bayliss and Starling that the young man had once been a newsboy on the streets of Boston. His fellow vendors of the daily papers recognized his unusual qualities and collected a fund which started him in Harvard College. The start was all he needed. Thereafter, through scholarships won by brilliant work and through his own efforts at earning money, he made his way both in the College and in the Medical School. A traveling fellowship gave him opportunity to study abroad. At the time of the visit in London he had already begun a career which developed into his being well known as an expert in diseases of the heart and blood vessels. Professor Starling was deeply interested in the story and remarked, "That would be difficult in England." It presented difficulties in the United States, but they were overcome. And the achievement made me proud of being able to recount it to my English friends.

It was during World War I that I became acquainted with the French physiologist, Charles Richet. He was a rather tall, gaunt man with a facial expression which seemed to indicate inquiry. There is no doubt that he was an extraordinary "original." Besides being a physiologist he had written poetry and plays, had advocated international pacifism, was a staunch believer in what he called "metapsychics" or spiritualism, and many years before the Wright brothers had flown successfully he had built an airplane which closely resembled the modern type. As related in a previous chapter, the Nobel prize was awarded to him for his observations on anaphylaxis. Although Richet himself was a pacifist, his sons were active in the war. One afternoon, while I was calling on him and we were engaged in a discussion, he arose and began pacing to and fro in the room. Finally he turned to me and said, "My dear Cannon, I talk of scientific matters but my heart is not in them. Three days have passed since my aviator son has been heard from. I am tormented by the thought that he may be alone and suffering." After expressing my deep sympathy for the distracted father I took my leave. A few days later the papers announced that young Richet had been found dead beside his crashed plane.

Although John Fraser was not a physiologist he was a medical investigator, and in my association with him at Béthune during the summer and early autumn of 1917, we studied together wounded men who were in shock; we walked together through the intricacies and charms of the old Burgundian city, discussing as we went; we played ring toss in the court of the hospital building; we sang songs with the rest of the group around the piano after dinner; and we hurried to the wards any time of the day or night when there was notice that a new and serious case had been brought in from the line. In a letter written home at that time I declared, "No truer friendship could grow between two men than that which has developed between us." Dr. Fraser was not the only Scot in the group. There were others, and also there was a lively Irish padre who liked nothing better than to bait them. "It's abominable," he would say, "how the Scotch run both sides of this war. Haig is a Scotchman. Mackensen, on the other side, is a Scotchman. And I'll bet that if you pronounced it right Hindenburg would be Hindenboro!" One evening the padre remarked that in a few years he would go to Edinburgh to call on Fraser. A portly butler would answer at the door. "Is Dr. Fraser at home?" "Do you mean *Sir* John Fraser?" the butler would reply. And the padre, all confused, would stammer an apology. Dr. Fraser laughed heartily with the rest of us over this jibe.

About a dozen years later Dr. Fraser, then Regius Professor of Surgery at the University of Edinburgh, came to the United States at a time when I was unable to greet him. I saw a notice of his visit in which he was referred to as Sir John Fraser. At once I wrote to him to ask if the padre's prediction had come true; if so, here were my congratulations. "Not true," he wrote. "The reporters confused surgeon and Sir John." Not many years passed before he was knighted, however, and later he was made a baronet. Though our paths have seldom crossed, my warm feeling of friendship for him has lasted through the passing decades and I have rejoiced over the well-deserved recognition of his sterling qualities.

Already I have told about my friendship with Juan Negrín of the University of Madrid, and its consequences in leading me to an interest in the Spanish Republic. That is a friendship which has continued firm and undiminished since our first meeting in 1930. We have actually met only twice during the intervening time, but the recurring holiday season in December brings a friendly message from him. I greatly admire him for his persistent confidence in a return of democratic government in Spain.

In 1934, Otto Loewi, whose classic demonstration of the chemical mediation of nerve impulses I have already described, accepted an invitation to lecture at the Harvard Medical School. That was the beginning of a friendship which has increased with the years. His plight when Hitler's forces seized control of Austria brought me into close acquaintance with the persecutions inflicted on scholars by the Germans. Besides being imprisoned, Dr. Loewi was compelled, in the presence of the Swedish minister, to sign away to the treasury of the Reich the money which he had received as a Nobel laureate and which he had left in Stockholm. After a while friends arranged his escape from Austria, but his wife was not allowed to follow him for nearly three years. At last they were reunited in New York City, where Dr. Loewi was given an honorable title and a place to work. For some months during the winter of 1944, I had the pleasure of associating with him. It was very moving to hear him express his admiration for the freedom of American democracy and for the generous attitude of American people toward refugee scholars. His enthusiasm, indeed, was at times almost embarrassing—I could not believe that we were as wonderful as he thought we were.

Professor B. A. Houssay of Buenos Aires, another friend for whom as a physiologist I have a very high regard, is one of the most outstanding contributors to science in the whole South

American continent. He has trained a host of disciples who have spread his influence widely. Three of them came to work at the Harvard laboratory; and in exchange young Harvard investigators have gone to him for inspiration and special training. He has been elected to the American Philosophical Society and to the National Academy of Sciences. It was a great gratification to me when his notable services to science were recognized and he was awarded an honorary degree at the Harvard Tercentenary Celebration. As men of liberal outlook he and some of our former students, who occupied professorial positions in Argentina, were among the 150 who petitioned the reactionary government in 1943 to adhere to democratic processes. Grim evidence of the willingness of a fascist group to commit intellectual suicide of their country was displayed when they deprived these professors of their positions as leaders in medical research and teaching.

While I was visiting professor of physiology at the Peking Union Medical School in 1935, I had the privilege of associating with Professor Robert K. S. Lim and of working with the remarkable group of young Chinese investigators he had gathered in the physiological laboratory. Dr. Lim had his academic and medical training at the University of Edinburgh and was a Chinese who talked English with a moderate Scotch accent. Although China can boast of a very ancient civilization, she is a young nation in recognizing the importance of modern science. Scarcely more than a score of years ago Dr. Lim established the first active center for physiological research in his native land. He also instituted an admirable periodical for reporting Chinese contributions to his science, *The Chinese Journal of Physiology.*

Besides being pioneer in a land that had neglected scientific methods, Dr. Lim has proved himself a devoted citizen and an ardent patriot. He had already started on a well-earned vacation when, in June, 1937, the Japanese military clique wantonly attacked the Chinese forces near Peking and thus started the long war between the two countries. At once Dr. Lim turned back from his vacation and began to apply his remarkable organizing gifts to the problem of providing medical and surgical care for the Chinese army. In view of the fact that in all China, with its population of perhaps four hundred million people, there are fewer well-trained doctors than in the city of New York, the need for such attention as Dr. Lim could give to military problems is obvious. One of his most praiseworthy achievements was the founding of more than a half-dozen training centers where young men could be taught the simpler procedures required for the care of wounded soldiers and fot treating the diseases from which both soldiers and civilians are likely to suffer. Although in the exigencies of the situation proper fundamental instruction, according to highest standards, was not possible, the graduates of these training centers have been able to perform urgently important services. American doctors attending American troops in China have bestowed high praise on the work done by the men taught in Dr. Lim's schools. It is altogether probable that these schools will exercise throughout the Chinese population a potent influence favorable to recognition of the values of modern medicine and surgery.

Dr. Lim is the son of a Chinese educator who was president of the University of Amoy. He comes, therefore, from intellectual antecedents and has the charm, the gracious courtesy, and the wide learning typical of the Chinese scholar. Yet, because of his organizing skill and efficiency he was appointed a lieutenant general in the Chinese army. On a brief visit to the United States, in 1944, he addressed the New York Academy of Medicine on methods of rehabilitating mutilated soldiers. At the end of his speech he received an ovation—the audience expressed their feeling toward him in repeated waves of applause. I count my friendship with Dr. Lim as one of my choicest.

No more kind or considerate reception have I had anywhere than that which I received from Professor Y. Sataké in Sendai, Japan, in 1935. For many years Dr. Sataké and his collaborators worked on problems associated with the functioning of the adrenal medulla, a subject on which the group at the Harvard Physiological Laboratory had worked for some time previously. It will be recalled that our results were in close agreement. Exchange of reprints of scientific papers and letters had laid a basis for our fellowship and understanding. At Sendai, Dr. Sataké entertained Mrs. Cannon and myself most charmingly. Among our very delightful experiences was participation in the quaint and elaborate Japanese tea ceremony, which he arranged for us in a dainty little house dedicated to that purpose. Later, as we went to the station to take the train for Tokyo, we were surprised and much pleased to find Dr. Sataké and his wife there to bid us goodbye. When I look back upon the evidences of good will shown by this gentle Japanese scholar I find it impossible to believe that he would approve the brutalities and sneaking deceits of the military group which has latterly dominated his government.

In certain respects the course of my investigations and those of the Russian physiologist, I. P. Pavlov, underwent a similar development. For years he and his collaborators studied the manner in which the digestive glands operate and are controlled. Because of dissatisfaction with the term "psychic secretion"—an undefined mental element applied to a physiological process—Pavlov was turned toward his extraordinarily detailed and extensive studies of behavior as determined by what he called "conditioned reflexes." My early studies, likewise, were concerned with digestive processes, but with emphasis on the mechanical effects produced by muscular contractions of the stomach and intestines. The stoppage of the contractions of the gastrointestinal tract in the presence of emotional excitement, as the reader knows, led me to become interested in the various other ways in which strong emotions can induce changes in the organism. The similarity of our studies resulted in correspondence between us. At the time of the Russian Revolution, when it was reported that Pavlov was suffering from inability to get food, I was able to collect about two thousand dollars which was sent to Professor Robert Tigerstedt, at Helsingfors, with the understanding that he would use it to provide for Pavlov's needs. Pavlov's son, Vladimir, later testified to the great value of this aid sent by American colleagues.

My first direct encounter with Pavlov was in 1923. He had come to this country with his son, who spoke excellent English. They had spent a few days in New York and were on the way to visit New Haven and Boston, when they suffered a most distressing experience. At the Grand Central Station they entered an empty coach of the New Haven train and were followed by three rough-looking men. One stood at the door as a guard. While the son was lifting the baggage up toward the rack, the other two seized Pavlov and quickly searched him. They snatched the wallet from a coat pocket of the defenseless man— he was near his seventy-fourth birthday—and before anything could be done, made their escape. In the wallet was over fifteen hundred dollars, possibly the remnant of the American contribution. Vladimir Pavlov still had some money, but not much. Father and son could only turn back and seek friends. They went to the Rockefeller Institute and explained what had happened. Professor Pavlov was as much affected by the indignity he had suffered as by the loss of his money. When asked what he would like to do, he said that he wanted to go to Boston and after that pay a short visit to the Woods Hole Biological Laboratory. That done, he wished to return to Russia where he would be safe! Arrangements were made for him and his son to carry out the program as far as Woods Hole. Meanwhile Dr. Richard M. Pearce telephoned to me to persuade them to accept, as other Europeans had done, the hospitality of the Rockefeller Foundation; it would permit them to carry out their original plans for travel in the United States. This I succeeded in doing.

I vividly recall the alert and eager look on Pavlov's face when, at the South Station in Boston, he limped vigorously toward me, with outstretched hands. After a stop at the Medical School and a brief survey of the physiological laboratory there, we went to my home in Cambridge. In the cool house we spent the hot July afternoon in reading and conversation. When evening came, we set forth for the Harvard Yard. Since my family was in New Hampshire the house was empty when we left it. As I closed the door behind me Pavlov inquired, "Where is the watchman?" I explained that there was no watchman. Seeing my old Ford car in the yard, he remarked, "Someone will steal your fine automobile." When I assured him there was no danger of that, he threw up his hands and exclaimed, "What a profound, what an abysmal difference there is between the morality of New York and the morality of Cambridge!"

On the way to Woods Hole, Pavlov "conditioned" a word for me. He spoke a rather simple German which I could understand and which I could fairly match. The man sitting in the seat in front of us held up a newspaper on which there was a large headline, stating that something was a fizzle. Pavlov turned to me and asked, "Was meint das Wort 'fitzel'? Fiasco?" I told him that his surmise was correct. Since then I never see the double z in a word without a sudden recall of the tz sound which Pavlov gave it, and the pleasant memory of that lively and keenly observant old man who sat beside me.

In 1929, Pavlov returned to Cambridge to attend the International Physiological Congress. He was the hero of the meeting. Though he was then eighty years of age, he seemed to have limitless energy. His presentation of the results of work in his laboratory and his conversations were marked by an astounding vigor of speech and intensity of gesticulation. A side of his nature which would not be revealed by expression of scientific interests appeared when, one evening at my home, he was told the tale, which is to be the subject of my next chapter, of an extraordinary series of accidents and misunderstandings that had alarmed my wife and sent solicitous friends to look for me in the Charles River. While others who heard the story were laughing at the humorous features of the complicated situation, the old man sat solemnly listening. And when the story was finished, he turned to Mrs. Cannon and expressed his sympathy for her in her anxiety.

I last saw Pavlov in Leningrad and Moscow at the meeting of the Physiological Congress in 1935. He was then eighty-six years old and yet preserved much of his former alertness and nervous activity. A day spent with him outside Leningrad at the immense new experimental establishment, built by the Soviet government for continuing his studies on the functions of the brain, was not to be forgotten. In the course of our conversation Pavlov sighed and expressed regret that the magnificent opportunity which was there offered had not come to him twenty years before. Had it been possible to reverse time he would then have been sixty-six years old, an age when commonly men of science are retired from active work!

In spite of the demands imposed upon Pavlov by the presidency of the Congress, he fulfilled the duties of his office with admirable grace and skill. It was obvious, however, that he was not a well man, as revealed by edema of the ankles. The Congress was held in August. The following February he died, a man as lovable as he was distinguished.

Of course, innumerable other friendships grew out of a long acquaintance with physiologists both in the United States and in foreign lands. I have intentionally selected for mention representatives of France, England, Scotland, Argentina, Austria, China, Japan, Spain, and Russia in order to illustrate how widely scientific interests reach forth and spread without regard to international boundaries and bring into more or less intimacy workers of different races and different nations.

# CHAPTER XVII

# A DISPLAY OF HUMAN FRAILTIES

THIS CHAPTER appertains to certain very human qualities of investigators—to the forgetfulness of a Physiologist and a Biochemist, to the ardent interest of a Pathologist, to the hospitality of a Philosopher, and to the sympathy and good will of a Physicist, a Zoologist and a Psychologist—that warped their calm and considerate judgments and sent them forth on an errand of quixotic gallantry. And it especially pertains to the unimaginative decision of the Physiologist, the worries of an anxious wife, and the wisdom of an Irish bridgetender. Incidentally, it illustrates how, in a world of facts, events can occur so perfectly linked in a complicated series that, unless authenticated, the linkage would hardly be accepted as real.

The occasion was a Saturday night in 1907. In the evening there was an important meeting of the faculty at the Harvard Medical School. The Physiologist had telephoned to his home that he would not appear for dinner. Just before the start of the meeting in the faculty room and while conversing with the Biochemist, the Physiologist suddenly recalled that he had left on his desk the agenda of the evening's affairs. The Biochemist simultaneously recalled that he had to go to his office in the same building to secure some papers he had forgotten, and he offered to pick up the Physiologist's papers on the way. The Physiologist then handed him his bunch of keys. On returning to the faculty room, the Biochemist handed to the Physiologist the agenda but forgot to return the keys. The Physiologist did not notice the omission.

The evening's deliberations were protracted and earnest.

After the meeting adjourned, the Physiologist and the Pathologist started away from the school together, continuing the animated discussion. It had not ended when the first streetcar stop was reached; and the two walked onward until they came to the Cottage Farm Bridge above the Charles River. In 1907 streetcars regularly passed over the bridge toward Cambridge. There was no car in sight, however, and the two friends decided to part. The Pathologist moved off toward his home; the Physiologist continued over the deserted bridge until he was overtaken by a streetcar, which he boarded.

When he reached home he found that, except for a light in the hall, the house was quite dark. He put his hand into his pocket for his keys—but they were not there; he then remembered that the Biochemist had not returned them. He rang the doorbell repeatedly, but roused no response. Going then beneath a window of his wife's bedroom in the second story, he picked up some gravel from the walk and threw it against the windowpane. Still no response. When he had repeated this effort a number of times without effect, he aptly recalled the interesting observations of Kohlschütter that the depth of sleep is much greater shortly after its beginning than it is later. In fact, Kohlschütter's own tests of the depth of sleep were performed by dropping a weight from different heights on a resounding plate of metal and finding that more noise was required to wake the sleeper during the first hour or two than later. The obvious strategy for the Physiologist, in the circumstances, was to wait until sleep had grown lighter and thereupon to try again to rouse the sleeper by ringing the bell or tossing more gravel. It was then about eleven o'clock.

The Physiologist decided, therefore, to idle away the time and return later. He walked down the silent street until he approached the home of the Philosopher. It was brightly lighted. From one of the windows smoke was pouring out. The situation at once attracted the Physiologist. He entered the open door and found the family much alarmed because the papers in a wastebasket had caught fire. When the excitement had died down the Physiologist explained his situation. He was at once invited to spend the night. His wife and sister at home were still soundly asleep, for a telephone call had just proved ineffective. They probably would not awaken until morning. Because of the difficulty of rousing them, acceptance of the Philosopher's invitation seemed to the frustrated Physiologist quite reasonable; he could sleep on the couch and return home at daybreak, before anybody had awakened. The Philosopher's mother inquired of the Physiologist whether his wife might not perhaps wake up in the night and be alarmed not to find her husband there.

"Oh, no," was the confident response, "she is not that kind of person."

So the Physiologist lay down and soon sank into peaceful slumber.

Now I turn to the other side of this tale. The Physiologist's wife and his sister had dinner together and, realizing that the evening was theirs alone, decided that it would be pleasant to go to a theater in Boston. In order to explain to the Physiologist their action, they left a note for him on the newel post in the hall. They returned from the theater about half past eleven o'clock and were somewhat surprised and disturbed that the Physiologist, whose domestic habits were eminently reliable, had not yet come home. For some time they sat waiting for him, while they engaged in desultory conversation and in frequent glances at the clock. Midnight came, and slowly minutes more passed away, but still no Physiologist. The situation obviously demanded action. First the telephone was put to use. The Physiologist's wife learned from various members of the faculty, who were roused from their slumber, that the Physiologist had been seen walking away from the meeting with the Pathologist. The Pathologist, likewise roused, reported that the Physiologist was last observed as he started across the Cottage Farm Bridge. One after another, the hospitals were canvassed for emergency cases of accident or injury, the streetcar company was asked about wrecks, and the police were interrogated about possible foul play. The police were especially concerned and wished to know everything that could be told about the Physiologist's disappearance. From none of these sources was any satisfactory clew obtained that might solve the mystery, now becoming graver. All reported that the night had been very quiet and without disturbance.

The disappearance at the bridge, however, seemed ominous. There certainly were suspicious circumstances. A few days previously the Physiologist had explained to his wife that he was prepaying the premium on his life insurance and that if anything should happen to him before the day the payment fell due, she was to collect the premium as well as the insurance. Furthermore, the Physiologist, like many another investigator, was subject to ups and downs, excitements and depressions, depending upon the way in which his researches were going. They had not been going altogether smoothly for some weeks. As the wife thought of the Cottage Farm Bridge and the Charles River, these memories led to dark forebodings. She felt she must have the counsel of friends.

Not far away lived the Physicist. The wife of the Physiologist, leaving his sister to attend to the telephone at home, went to ask the Physicist's advice. It was then about one o'clock in the morning. She awakened the Physicist, told him the whole story, and awaited his judgment. In the spiritless voice of one hardly awake, he said, "I'm sorry, but I can't offer you much hope." He agreed, however, to dress, collect other friends, and go with her to the fateful bridge.

They passed the Philosopher's house without stopping, because they had heard that one of the children was ill and that the elder members of the family were worn out taking care of him. It was only kind and considerate, therefore, to spare the Philosopher. The next person to be awakened and told the sad tale was the Zoologist; he was soon ready to accompany them. The three then went to the home of the Psychologist. When his awareness was well established and he had heard the story, he dressed and joined the group. No streetcars were running. There was no way of reaching the bridge except by walking about two miles. As they drew near it, the Psychologist, who had thoughtfully brought along a candle, lighted it now and again to peer into dark places behind fences and in cellarways, searching for a corpse. When the party reached the bridge the Psychologist, now impressed by the importance of finding the floating body, stepped into a small boat on the riverbank and poled himself out into the stream. He examined carefully the shores below the bridge and poked among the piles that served as its support. The boat was partly full of oily and muddy water. The Psychologist in his eagerness paid no attention to that circumstance until the next day when he noted the rings of black stain that had ruined his trousers—one of the minor disasters of the Physiologist's disappearance.

The Zoologist had recently been reading *The Adventures of Sherlock Holmes* and had been convinced that by thorough analysis and scrupulous study of the evidence any mystery could be solved. The important matter was to map out the bridge into definite areas and then to examine in detail each of the areas for signs of a struggle. This he did with great care. The results were not rewarding.

Somehow the rumor that the Physiologist had mysteriously disappeared from the Cottage Farm Bridge had spread until it reached two medical students. As dawn was breaking they arrived and, taking in the situation at a glance, they noted that the tide in the river had long been rising. Filled with pride in their shrewd observation they argued that the body should not be sought immediately under the bridge or downstream, as the Psychologist had done, but rather, upstream. Accordingly they made their way along the miry and sedgy banks of the Charles for a considerable distance, accumulating filth on shoes and clothing but finding no evidence for their theory.

The searchers on and near the bridge were joined after a time by the Irish bridgetender and a companion, to whom the told the story of their search. He made light of their anxiety and pointed out that it was Saturday night. The investigators were somewhat mystified by the explanatory implication of "Sattidy night." Slowly it dawned that the bridgetender had associates to whom Saturday night offered opportunity for a different sort of behavior than is permitted on other nights.

"Probably he's gone with some friends to have a drink," he said.

"Oh, but he doesn't drink," protested the Physiologist's wife.

"You say he's a doctor?" answered the bridgetender. "They know lots of things to take."

The bridgetender's companion was more sympathetic. "Don't you worry," he said, "I know just how you feel. My brother disappeared for more than two weeks, but I found him. He was safe in a hospital with both legs cut off."

At last the Physicist, the Zoologist, and Psychologist and the Physiologist's wife became hopeless, and they wearily trudged the long distance back to their homes. Friends had gathered at the house of the Physiologist to offer such consolation as was possible in so tragic a situation. Food and stimulants were brought to the worn and distracted wife; her hands were held by sympathetic and solicitous comforters; and tender words of consolation were spoken to her.

This melancholy scene was interrupted by a ring at the doorbell. The Physiologist, refreshed by a good night's sleep, had awakened early, had quietly risen, and had hastened to his home. Hardly was the door opened by his sister, fully dressed, before he heard his name shouted by her, three times, at the top of her voice. Mystified faces peered over the balustrade and gazed in stupefaction from parlor and kitchen. There was a scurry of footsteps in a room above; his wife rushed precipitately down the stairs and, as indignant as she was pleased, threw herself into his arms.

The newspaper reporters did not let the incident pass unnoticed. They had consulted the police and learned vaguely what had happened. In an account published the next day the disappearance of a Harvard professor was described, and the statement ended, "The explanation *given* was that he spent the night at the home of a friend."

This unusual series of incidents made a chain the links of which held tightly. There were at least sixteen points at which a break in the chain would have avoided a tragicomedy, an anxious night, and hours of painful search by a group of solicitous friends. Not a break occurred. Every one of them can be thoroughly vouched for. The remarkable series clearly proves that facts are sometimes as strange and unlikely in their relations as are any fancies of the imagination.

The foregoing story is included in this volume on traits of investigators in order to disclose both their frailties and their benevolence. The forgetful Physiologist allowed his knowledge to lead him astray when he laid too much emphasis on the early depth of sleep. He went sadly wrong again in assuming that he would not be missed if he remained away from his home. And the hardy company of explorers who spent hours of the night tramping to the suspected bridge and searching the black waters beneath it did not carefully consider the character of the Physiologist nor the testimony of all the agencies which were consulted that nothing harmful had happened that night. To the credit of their sympathy they succumbed to the anxieties of the Physiologist's wife. The judgment of all of them in affairs of the laboratory was excellent, but in a social situation emotional elements were allowed to exercise an overwhelming influence. Only the bridgetender seems to have preserved a wise attitude, for he remarked, after hearing the tale from the worried explorers, "Why don't you give a man a chance to come home?"

# CHAPTER XVIII

# DOINGS IN IDLENESS

ALL WORK and no play makes Jack a dull boy, and grown-up John a dull investigator. This prudential dictum, however, may receive scant respect from scientific explorers who are ardently in pursuit of an alluring fresh lead. In those circumstances persistent striving seems the only satisfactory way of spending time. It is noteworthy that intense application has different effects on persons whose inner drive dominates them. Some there are so favorably organized that they become tired, as they properly should, and are compelled to stop by sheer failure of their brains to operate. Others there are whose eagerness and endeavors become all the more fierce the longer they persist in an exciting chase. I happen to belong in this latter group. By great good fortune my marriage to Cornelia James blessed me with a devoted counselor and companion who, wisely and expertly, knew when to loosen my grip on affairs in the laboratory and draw me away to sunshine and refreshing exploits. In my sane periods she and I have the same ideas of enjoyable recreation—finding novel adventures in vigorous outdoor sports. We began this sort of recreation from the start of our life together and have resorted to it often ever since.

Canoeing and mountain climbing were continued as diversions during the early years of my professional career. Paddling a canoe along a sylvan stream and mastering a conspicuous height both bring rewards in memorable pleasures. Around the next curve in a meandering river there is likely to be something new and enchanting—a deer drinking at the brink or a family of ducklings swimming along serenely, led by the mother bird. And at each stop on a trail up a mountainside the glory of wide vistas is an exhilarating reward for the effort. I have canoed not only on the sluggish waters of the Charles near Boston but also on the wild currents of Minnesota and Wisconsin streams. Canoeing on the ocean offers excitements which the quiet waters of a river or of a small lake do not afford. This is especially true when the uneasy surface of the sea is expressed in long sweeping swells. The tiny craft is then repeatedly lifted to tremulous heights, only to be dropped to depths which make the oncoming roller appear ominous and engulfing. It is a stirring sport, but not to be engaged in without due caution. Wherever one may be, there is a thrill that comes as one strikes his paddle into the water and feels the quick response of the light craft, which "a hand may launch, a hand restrain." The attractions of driving onward in a canoe offer an almost irresistible invitation whenever that opportunity is presented.

In 1903, my wife and I were in England on our way to attend a meeting of the British Association for the Advancement of Science. As we were wandering about Oxford we stumbled upon a Canadian canoe at a boathouse on the Thames. Here was a chance! We found that we could rent the canoe for a trip down the river and could easily ship it back from any point that might be convenient. We clinched the bargain then and there, put our meager baggage into the bark, and pushed off.

Along the quiet stream we paddled, passing the heavy punts in which young people were enjoying themselves; and we wondered why they preferred to pole their way slowly instead of flitting along as we did in our lighter craft. Soon we were going by the loveliest possible lawns which swept back from the river's edge to stately houses set among magnificent old trees. At one point we were surprised to see a typical Venetian gondola with a gondolier, in black suit and red sash, standing at the stern and, in leisurely swings of his body, propelling downstream two elegantly dressed ladies in Gainsborough hats. They looked casually at us as we scurried past.

It was not long before we came to a lock. This offered us a novel experience. When we entered the enclosure at the upper level of the water the lock master promptly appeared and informed us that a few pence were required to let us down. Soon the gates were closed behind us and we felt ourselves slowly sinking until we were entirely surrounded by the grim walls and gates as in a huge dark box. Then the lower gates majestically opened and set us free. The experience, whenever it was repeated, was impressive. The volume of water in the lock seemed so prodigious compared with the tiny canoe which was being lowered that we never felt quite reconciled to the huge shift required in order that we might go onward. The lock keepers, however, always appeared quite satisfied as long as we paid the small fee. And with a wave of farewell we would slip away.

When we reached the historic Henley course there was a strong wind blowing at our backs. As a precaution against the weather we had brought with us a large, strong, family umbrella. The idea of using the umbrella as a sail was natural enough. In order to prevent the wind from turning it inside out, I fastened the ends of the ribs to the handle with string. My wife, seated in the bow of the canoe, held the umbrella in front of her; at the stern, I employed the paddle as a rudder. Thus equipped we went speeding over the Henley course. Unfortunately we did not know the exact starting point nor the location of the goal. We were unable to report, therefore, whether we made a record run which should be registered in the books, but certainly we traversed the stretch of water at high speed.

Our Baedeker warned persons boating on the Thames to "beware of the weirs and lashers." A notion of the meaning of weirs was not beyond us. But lashers were something new. In order to obtain enlightenment we stopped our paddling in front of an elderly man who sat on the bank, holding a pole, and patiently awaiting a nibble. I asked him if he would kindly tell me the difference between a weir and a lasher. He pushed back his tattered straw hat, removed the pipe from his mouth, rubbed his chin with the back of his hand, and remarked sententiously, "Why, one's a weir and t'other's a lasher." To this day I do not know what a lasher is—and would not for worlds inquire further.

On Sunday evening we reached the enchanting English village of Marlow and decided to spend the night there. Leaving the canoe at a boathouse near the bridge, we walked along the main street toward the village inn. As we approached the inn a man emerged from its portal, walked to a neighboring building, and began to pull a rope and ring a bell. When we came up to him, he informed us that he was the innkeeper but that there was a fire and we should have to wait until the firemen were started before he could attend to us. He continued ringing the bell for some time. Finally a man appeared, dressed in a greenish blue uniform with trousers tucked in high boots. As he opened the doors of what proved to be the fire-engine house adjoining the inn, he remarked casually that someone should go for horses. A youth standing near volunteered for that service and ran off. Meanwhile another man in uniform came up and the two lifted the heavy tongue of the fire engine and set it in place. Then they pulled off from the wall a large sheet which covered brass-buckled harness. Soon a hack drawn by two horses was driven into the scene. The horses were unhitched, their harness was removed and replaced by the brassy harness taken from the wall. Then they were backed into position in front of the fire engine and fastened in place. Thereupon they were led forth so that the engine was in the clear outside the house. Meanwhile other uniformed and booted men had gathered. One of them climbed to the top of the engine while the others lined up beside it. The man on the engine then tossed to each man on the ground a green bag containing a heavy object. The bags were carefully opened and from each there was withdrawn a brass helmet in a high state

of polish. When the helmets had been put on and the bags had
been thrown back to the top of the engine, the man who had
caught them opened another bag, containing a bugle. He
sounded a few notes on the bugle which were the signal for
the firemen to get aboard. As soon as they were in place, the
driver took up the reins and the party started off.

My wife, who has many of the qualities of a reformer,
promptly turned to the innkeeper and anxiously inquired,
"Wouldn't it be better if the men did not wait to put on their
uniforms but started at once to get the engine to the fire?"

"Oh, yes," he replied, "it would be better, but those are the
regulytions." And that was that!

We continued paddling on our way until at last we arrived
in sight of the ancient pile of Windsor Castle. It was really exciting to see the familiar outline of that historic structure at a
distance and to move toward it and to watch it grow greater
and more impressive as we came nearer. To anyone wishing to
get the full flavor of that scene the approach down the Thames
can be warmly recommended.

My wife and I have tramped not only in the Montana mountains but also in the Canadian Rockies. And we had one memorable experience in walking across the Monte Moro Pass from
Saas Fee in Switzerland to Macugnaga in Italy. As we reached
the last stopping place, a rough stone hut far in the glacial
rubble on the Swiss side, we found in the book which travelers
had signed, the following note, "From Saas Fee to Macugnaga
under a glorious sky" and signed "Henry P. Bowditch" and
"Hugh Kronecker"—two distinguished physiologists, fast
friends, one of them my predecessor in the Harvard Medical
School. We had been informed that one of the most impressive
mountain views anywhere was the east face of Monte Rosa
which one beholds in the descent from the top of the pass to
the little Italian town. We looked forward eagerly to that inspiring spectacle, but the fates were against us. When we
reached the top of the pass the mist was so thick that only by

noticing the trail of rust on the bare rocks, where hobnails had left their particles which had turned red, did we find our way to the worn path leading downward. As we descended, swirls of mist would occasionally reveal high cliffs on one side and a deep abyss on the other.

On our way we came to two rude stone huts. Birds flew away from one of them and we hastily concluded that the huts must be empty. Soon we were startled to hear sounds from within the larger hut; our apprehensions promptly subsided, however, when soldiers in Italian uniform emerged. They were the border guards. One of the soldiers offered to guide us on our way, but we gratefully turned the offer aside and continued by ourselves. It might have been better if we had accepted the soldier's offer, for we soon entered a larch wood where, in the evening shadow of Monte Rosa, it was so dark that we could not see the path but had to shuffle along in its depression, feeling the way with our feet. Finally we reached the end of the wood and in spite of the darkness could see the path as a lighter band distinguishable from the ground on either side. We were then in high hopes of being near to the end of our journey, until we heard far below us the faint ringing of a church bell. Hours passed, however, before we stumbled into the hotel at Macugnaga, thoroughly exhausted. I have always regretted not having seen the famous eastern face of Monte Rosa.

Tramping in the New England mountains is a milder, less vigorous sport than in the higher and rockier ranges of our West or of Switzerland. Although less exacting, they provide opportunities for good exercise, glorious views, and the lasting satisfactions of pleasant companionship. I enjoy very happy memories of tramping in the New Hampshire and Vermont mountains with Ralph Perry, philosopher, with David Edsall, physician, and with Harvey Cushing, John Hartwell, and Fred Murphy, surgeons. With the last three I once had a toilsome adventure in an excursion from the old Profile House over the mountain which bears the Great Stone Face, to a spot which on the map is labeled Lonesome Lake. It was reported that no one had gone that way for six decades. The descent of a cliff by pulling treetops toward us and clambering down the trunks, and the later fierce struggle through a tangle of blown-down pines, dry and stiff with age, and through thick underbrush, was too strenuous for any of us at our years. Dr. Murphy and Dr. Hartwell, former Yale football players, testified that the demands on strength and endurance equaled those of a first-rate football game. A trip which we thought might take three hours occupied in fact more than twice that time. It left us with such holes in our clothing as to require us to deploy in a special formation when we approached the hotel.

Avocations of later years have been less strenuous. Elsewhere I have mentioned boyhood acquaintance with the use of carpenter's tools. The making of furniture—tables, bookcases, couches, and desks—has proved both a useful and an enjoyable diversion. The employment of one's skill in making objects which have practical use is a great satisfaction, for they are fairly permanent evidences of temporary activity. Gardening offers another sort of satisfaction, in providing hopefulness and anticipation. Joseph Jefferson once testified to the pleasures of gardening for an old man; it invited him to look forward from the spring when he plants the seeds to the autumn when he garners the crops, and thence to the spring again while he plans for the coming season. He can always hope to live each short interval as he edges along to his final days. The disadvantage of gardening is the necessity of keeping it "wed," as the New Hampshire farmers put it. And if witch grass creeps in, there is endless attention that must be given to prevent the overwhelming of the planted seeds by the totalitarian grass.

An advantage of gardening, especially if one has to spend considerable time cultivating growing things, is the opportunity it offers for meditation. In former times, when the ox cart was a means of locomotion or even in horse-and-buggy days, the slow movement from place to place yielded time for ideas to be ruminated and mellowed and for fresh associations to be established among them. It is said that the physiologist, Goltz, testified that his most important work was done while he was fishing. As he waited for the fish to bite, plans for experiments were gradually elaborated. He had freedom to think of the consequences of a possible result of one sort or of possible results of other sorts, coming from an experimental test, until he had so refined and limited the procedure that the experiment when performed would have critical value. Gardening, as one quietly engages in it, presents the same detachment from distracting affairs that fishing does and allows central interests to come to the surface of consciousness and to be appreciated.

Some years ago I was advised to take life more easily during the summer vacation than I had been in the habit of doing. It happened that my children had been inspired to engage in modeling in clay through an interest taken in them by a neighbor, Miss Louisa Eyre, the sculptress. I decided that this was a sufficiently different pursuit from that to which I was accustomed, to qualify as recreation. The softening of the clay, the arrangement of supporting structures, and the initial stages of outlining a head and neck proved fascinating. My first model was a little girl of five years who could be persuaded to pose only by being permitted to chew gum. This situation presented difficulties as the time was reached for modeling the face and especially the mouth. When I appealed to the child to stop the chewing motion for a few moments while I caught her face in repose, she insisted on parking the gum under her upper lip. The result of my efforts was recognizable as human but hardly as a striking likeness. If I had been more skillful I suppose I might have caught her in her act so that the likeness could have been labeled, "Little Girl Chewing Gum."

Later I was more successful, in making a portrait bust of my youngest daughter, Helen. She had to be bribed with sweet chocolate but she ate it between poses; accordingly it did not have the baneful effects of the more persistent gum. As may be known to some readers, there exist in a number of cities of the country physicians' art associations. These groups periodically hold exhibits of sketches, paintings, and sculptures which members of the profession have produced. With considerable temerity, urged on by my family, I entered the bust of Helen at a Boston exhibit, under the title, "A Young Girl." To my surprise and delight I received about eight inches of blue ribbon, a token which I have prized as much as any other honor that has ever come to me.

There was a time when the Boston Symphony concerts were a source of pleasure, but for me, as was true of William James, they gradually lost their charm. Even when I most enjoyed them, however, they proved to be stimulating to extraneous thoughts—thoughts concerned with scientific problems—rather than with appreciation of the music itself. I have had the same experience in attending lectures and occasionally in listening to sermons. In all these instances, including gardening and fishing, the freedom from usual demands on time and attention appears to be the essential condition.

Among diversions, general reading must be assigned a prominent place. Individuals vary greatly in the sorts of literature they find most engaging and worth while. As a youth and young man I enjoyed greatly the reading of serious novels, especially the English and American classics. Later a novel and particularly a new novel must have acquired the reputation of being quite exceptional before I could be persuaded to spend time perusing it. Gradually, in the course of years, biography and historical studies have come to occupy chief place in my attention. Biography has held particular interest because it reveals the influences which have affected the lives of men and tells how they have met the problems which have confronted them— the critical judgments and actions which have led to their success or failure. One of my deepest satisfactions has been reading about Abraham Lincoln; various accounts of his remarkable career and treatises on special features of it have given me many hours of absorbing interest.

Perhaps I reveal a weakness when I confess to being bored

by the ordinary detective story, for that seems to be a solace
during the idle hours of many of my betters. So frequently,
however, the means of identifying the culprit are trivial and
incidental or quite misleading, that when the story ends I feel
that I have been less entertained than tricked.

During my years as a student at the Harvard Medical School
I was a proctor in the old Foxcroft House, then partly used as
a dormitory. One day an ingenuous and confiding undergraduate sat down in my room and told me that his father had impressed upon him the importance of avoiding the sowing of
wild oats in order that he might have a good chance later of
playing with his children. That, the father had explained, was
one of the greatest joys life would grant. This prediction I have
found to be true. Fortunately the simple diversions I have enjoyed—working with tools, making kites and little boats and
doll houses, modeling clay, canoeing, and tramping in the hills
—are such as can be shared joyously with the young. To see in
my children expressions of delight in the occupations which
have given delight to me is deeply gratifying and the shared
enjoyments establish bonds of companionship which have permanent and incalculable values.

If, perchance, one's powers of application and endurance
wane as the years pass by, one may take comfort in a resort to
diversions which have been cultivated during earlier periods.
Not infrequently an investigator who has developed gentle
hobbies as diversions has been compelled in middle age to surrender them because of lack of time. Return to them in the
freedom of the final years offers a renewal of the interests of
youth and gives solace and recreation when other possibilities
are fading away.

# CHAPTER XIX

# MANY HAPPY RETURNS

THERE are critics who have assumed that scientific investigators are a cold-blooded tribe dwelling in laboratories where the prevailing motives are objectivity, detachment, dispassionateness, skepticism. Admittedly, observations and judgments are kept as impersonal and unprejudiced as possible during efforts to learn what is true, for experience has proved that unless scrupulous care is exercised, bias, due to perhaps unrecognized personal interests and preconceptions, has subtle ways of affecting eyes and ears and the selection of descriptive words and thus vitiating the precise report of events. These precautions are necessary also because there is another powerful motive which pushes hard on determined indifference and neutrality—the burning human desire to know whether the idea has predicted a fact. When that proves to be true, enthusiasm may be boundless.

Primary among the rewards of the scientific explorer is the discovery of a new phenomenon. Only he who has had the experience knows the thrill of it. A friend, who was in Faraday's laboratory when the influence of the earth's magnetism on a wire conducting an electric current was being tested, has written, "All at once Faraday exclaimed, 'Do you see, do you see, do you see!' as the small wire began to revolve . . . I shall never forget the enthusiasm expressed in his face and the sparkling in his eyes." Kepler realized the joy which compensates the investigator for all his efforts when he completed the evidence that established his third law of planetary motion. Even one whose pulses have not quickened with the excitement of

discovery can understand how he must have felt as he burst
into triumphant exultation:

What I prophesied two-and-twenty years ago, that for which I
devoted the best part of my life to astronomical contemplations, I
have brought to light and recognized its truth beyond my most
sanguine expectations. It is not eighteen months since I got the
first glimpse of light, three months since the dawn, very few days
since the unveiled sun burst upon me. Nothing holds me; I will
indulge my sacred fury. If you forgive me, I rejoice; if you are
angry, I can bear it. The die is cast, the book is written, to be
read either now or by posterity, I care not which. It may well wait
a century for a reader, as God has waited six thousand years for
an observer.

A similar emotion of delight overwhelmed Pasteur when he
separated optically active crystals of a substance into two modifications of identical chemical compositions but of different
physical properties—a discovery which formed the basis for the
great field of stereochemistry. He was so deeply moved that he
left his laboratory, "seeking for someone to whom he could
communicate the joy in his mind."

The marvel of beholding for the first time a fresh aspect of
nature fascinates the investigator and, even through privation
and struggle and repeated disappointments, the possibility
tends to hold him strictly to the search. This single-mindedness
in striving for new knowledge involves a large degree of neglect
of the motives for money-getting. After all, new knowledge—
knowledge in its unprofitable infancy—obviously does not possess commercial value. The vast majority of mankind are well
satisfied with what they know. There is no demand from them
that their relative ignorance be increased by further additions
to the accumulated information available to the race. During
nearly twenty years the Dutch botanist, De Vries, investigated
the origin of variations in plants. His discoveries threw much
light on the processes of biological evolution. If money were
the motive, who would labor twenty years in order at the end

to publish a book which only university libraries and a few meagerly paid biologists would care to buy?

No intelligent person would for a moment think that research in "pure" science, which has been motivated by personal curiosity and which, though satisfying that curiosity, has not resulted in immediately useful discoveries, is destined to have little or no economic value. There are too many examples all about us illustrating the fact that increased knowledge of nature yields increased power over her processes. The mathematical predictions of Maxwell and the experiments of Hertz made possible the elaborate modern development of wireless transmission which brings news and entertainment to myriads of homes and protects the lives of travelers on land and sea. The two men were not concerned with possible commercial value of their studies. The motive impelling them was the scientific motive, the desire for understanding. Such men may be grateful that accumulated wealth gave them leisure to carry on their investigations, free from the worries of uncertain livelihood; but they would look upon eagerness for money without envy. This attitude should not be regarded as implying a claim of moral superiority, for the investigator is in the happy position of doing his specially chosen work and receiving a livelihood in addition. This livelihood is not lavish, to be sure; if it is sufficient to meet the simple requirements and tastes of the investigator and his family, it is enough.

A story attributed to the late William J. Mayo, famous surgeon, illustrates the range of compensation of various groups in the medical profession. As he approached the place where a meeting of doctors was being held, he saw some elegant limousines and remarked, "The surgeons have arrived." Then he saw some cheaper cars and said, "The physicians are here, too." A few scattered model-T Fords led him to infer that there were pathologists present. And when he saw a row of overshoes inside, under the hat rack, he is reported to have remarked, "Ah, I see there are laboratory men here." Although members of the same faculty, I have rarely heard the "laboratory men" express envy of the surgeons and the physicians (harassed by duties to hospital trustees, to patients and anxious relatives, to the medical school organization, to students, and finally to research interests) for the greater money return which they receive. Many years ago, at a dinner attended by some physicians and surgeons, the conversation turned to what each of them would do if he had all the money he wanted. One of the surgeons turned to me and asked me what I would do. I remember that I answered, "I *have* all the money I want. My wife gives me ten dollars a month and with that I pay my carfare, buy my lunches, and get my hair cut." This reply, which amused my companions, was a simple statement of fact. In compensation for smaller incomes the laboratory men have security of tenure in their appointments, commonly a pension on retiring, and, besides, an allotment of free time for investigation. The last advantage is of highest value. When one of my colleagues, Otto Folin, and I were offered elsewhere salaries three times the amount we had been receiving, we did not feel that we were making a sacrifice by refusing the increased pay; we chose to remain where we were assured complete liberty in following our personal research programs.

I do not claim that all investigators at all times can be indifferent to betterment of their financial status. They may have been accustomed to expensive ways which are hard to change, they may have growing families which become costly, and they may have dependents who fall ill and therefore necessitate earning more money. These conditions are especially influential on young investigators who have given "hostages to fortune." Opportunities for meeting oppressive costs may be offered in higher salaries paid by hospital, municipal, and state laboratories, by medical institutes and by pharmaceutical establishments. President Conant of Harvard University, addressing members of the American Chemical Society, warned them of risks which might ensue from inconsiderate continuance of such transfers:

Remember that you are dealing in your laboratories with the application of science; you must look to the universities for the fundamental advances which you later apply. Secondly, you must each year look to the universities for trained men. Therefore, if you raid the university staffs and pick off the promising young professors for your work, you are endangering your greatest assets.

Trained chemical investigators are probably more in demand for extra-academic labor than are their medical colleagues. In practice, however, the situation of the two groups is the same. In medical schools the department of pharmacology is especially vulnerable. In fairness, universities as well as industrial concerns should be asked to make adjustments.

Whatever may be the pros and cons of adequate payment of scientific men, whose investigations may be of very great value to industry, the fact to be emphasized is that they do not enter on scholarly careers with the idea of making money and obviously they continue in scholarly careers for other than financial reasons.

What now can be said about other returns in the life of a scientific explorer? Elsewhere I have called attention to friendships in various parts of the world which result from community of interests, from use of similar methods, and from the securing of related results. The bonds of mutual friendship and respect thus established hold collaborators together in an enduring brotherhood. These collaborators understand each other's aims and can appreciate the value of each other's labors. In this brotherhood the investigator regards his good name as more precious than great riches. And in the sympathy and close comradeship of others who share with him the aims of the truth seeker, the investigator finds a large part of his reward.

Related to the community of interests and the sympathetic understanding which exist among scientific workers is the recognition one receives by being elected to membership in learned societies at home and abroad and by participation in the long sequence of lectures associated with the founders of historic lectureships. In so far as these tributes offer opportunities for meeting with fellow scientists and exchanging with them ideas and reports of achievements, they present a pleasant form of recognition of the efforts the investigator has made to promote his science.

Fame as a reward of scientific endeavor is not to be relied upon. There are too many instances in human history that show only a belated recognition of the importance of observations of new phenomena. Decades passed before the significance of Mendel's studies on the principles of inheritance was properly evaluated. Furthermore, with passing years the names of investigators are likely to become incidental and dissociated from the work they have done. I can regard philosophically the fact that already my relation to early use of the Röntgen rays in studies of gastrointestinal functions has been largely forgotten. Possibly indicative of approaching oblivion was an experience I had in 1935, when crossing the Pacific on my way to the Peking Union Medical School. A young student of biology on shipboard happened to pick up in the library of the ship's surgeon a book in which there was reference to observations on the movements of the alimentary canal made by someone named Cannon, in 1897. The young man brought the book to me and in all innocence inquired, "Was he your *father?*"

An investigator who has had the happy advantage of receiving and training young disciples reaps a rich reward in knowing that those whom he has disciplined have taken positions of responsibility and often themselves have established centers of influence. An example of such gratifying diffusion of a fructifying influence was offered by Karl Ludwig, who for decades made Leipzig a center to which young physiologists were welcomed without prejudice of geographical or racial origins. They flocked to his laboratory and were inspired by his example as a single-minded lover of truth. Doubtless his students contributed to his achievements as he contributed to theirs. They brought to him willing hands, new points of view, and the enthusiasm of youth; and he gave them the benefits of his insight, his skill, and his large experience. Both he and they profited from the fresh projects which naturally develop when there is free and open conference of men imbued with common interests. Through his students, Ludwig's inspiring ideas and his fine example were diffused to many countries; for the physiologists whose careers he affected returned to their homes to continue the studies they had begun under him. Ludwig and his time contrast strikingly with later practices in Germany. In the presence of the pervasive and universal value of truth-seeking the barriers of exclusive nationalism are strange and anomalous. They stand for folly instead of wisdom. Every nation can profit from the advantages which flow from a free interchange of students and ideas. We have all received benefits from the past; it is appropriate to recognize that we all owe equally a service to the future.

It happens that by good fortune I have had the satisfaction of seeing young investigators who have worked in the Harvard Physiological Laboratory go elsewhere and take charge of laboratories on their own responsibility. Among the places to which I could travel and be welcomed as a former collaborator are Galveston, New York City, Philadelphia, San Francisco, Hanover, New Haven, Charlottesville, Columbus, Nashville, Baltimore, Worcester, Buffalo, Chicago, and two Rochesters— of New York and of Minnesota. To these may be added Rosario and Cordoba in Argentina, Mexico City and Puebla in Mexico, Montreal in Canada, Santiago in Chile, São Paulo in Brazil, and, until the catastrophes of World War II, Amsterdam in Holland, Liége in Belgium, Debrecen in Hungary, Manila in the Philippine Islands, Chengtu in China, Marseilles and Paris in France, and formerly Vienna in Austria and Barcelona and Santiago de Compostela in Spain. My Spanish students sided with the Republic and are now refugees from their native land because of their passionate love of liberty.

Associated with the common arrangement whereby the investigator is also a teacher is the pleasure, after decades of teaching, of meeting former students almost everywhere one goes. I have already told about motoring through dilapidated Verdun with Dr. Simon Flexner and the late Dr. Alexander Lambert on Armistice Day, 1918. An obstruction in the road stopped us for a moment before a passageway leading down into a cellar. While we waited, up from the darkness came one of my former students. As I was walking along the sidewalk in Haymarket, London, a taxi screeched to a sudden stop and the passenger inside shouted my name and waved to me. He was another of my former students. On arriving in Honolulu I was entertained by two of my students, who showed me the beauties of Oahu. And on reaching the quay at Shanghai there awaiting me was Dr. J. Heng Liu, an admirable physician who had been taught physiology by me and who at the time of my visit was health commissioner of the Chinese Republic. When the International Physiological Congress met in Leningrad and Moscow in 1935, I was at one time surrounded by persons who had studied physiology at the Harvard Medical School. I have rejoiced in a warm feeling of being among friends as I have gone about the world and happened upon men with whom I had associated in the laboratory and in conferences. This is a very pleasant return for long years of instruction, a reward many an old teacher has enjoyed.

The discoverer in science may justifiably entertain the deeply gratifying thought that work well done, observations carefully made and recorded, will ultimately combine with other observations, perhaps made long afterward, in forming the body of truth. The conquest of yellow fever, for example, involved the identification of mosquitoes, and that in turn depended on previous descriptions by entomologists who had studied scales and veins on the wings, and hairs on the bodies of the insects in order to classify them. Little did they realize how their descriptions would fit into the strategy of abolishing a devastating disease. An investigator may never see the synthesis which brings his work into its relations with the work of others, but from historical evidence he can be assured that such may be the destiny of his observations. If, perchance, the labors in which he engages result in immediately practical consequences beneficial to all mankind, he has the happiness of knowing that there will be a continuing beneficence long after his own labors have ceased. There is great reward in the thought of these "durable results of the perishable years."

Another reward, sometimes bestowed on the worker in science, is that of seeing during his lifetime the value of his services in the relief of human need. When Davy made discoveries in combustion which enabled him to invent the safety lamp for miners, he knew that toilers in the darkness of the mines would thereby be protected in future times from dangers of violent death. When Faraday, near the end of his life, saw the tower of a lighthouse illuminated by means of a huge dynamo, one of the results of his fundamental discovery of electrical induction, he experienced a deep satisfaction in the thought that it might be the means of saving many human lives. And in the realm of medical science, how great must have been the joy of Koch and of Pasteur when, after age-long strivings to solve the mystery of disease, they saw the consequences of their research and could realize that in time humanity might no longer be scourged with plague and pestilence and driven hopelessly to death because of unknown agents of infection. Similar satisfactions have doubtless been experienced by the discoverers of means of overcoming diabetes, pernicious anemia, general paresis, and many another disorder.

The reward of beholding useful consequences of my own scientific studies cannot be regarded as great, because only in the common use of a heavy powder mixed with food—the bismuth meal—to reveal disorders of the digestive tract when it is examined with the X-rays, have there been clear and definite consequences. In addition there was, to be sure, some gratification in finding that the co-operative work on wound shock during World War I and later in the Harvard Physiological Laboratory had values for the wounded in World War II. And it is said that our researches on the bodily effects of emotions have been helpful because they give the doctor pertinent information in explaining to his nervous patients the reasons for their functional disorders. All I can testify is that in as far as the investigations with which I have been concerned have had any practical utility, I am much pleased.

Though the scientific explorer has no prospect of becoming rich in the worldly sense, as a result of his labors, he certainly enjoys a rich life. The enthralling pleasures of discovery, the opportunity to do what he would rather do than anything else in the world, the sense of security in his academic position, the freedom for study and investigation, the world-wide friendships, the homage from learned societies, the assurance that his efforts in teaching and seeking have social value—all these satisfactions are his. No man could ask for better recompense.

# CHAPTER XX

# THE FRUITFUL YEARS

WHAT is an investigator's most creative period? At what time of life is he likely to make his most important contributions? R. S. Woodworth, the psychologist, has declared, "Seldom does a very old person get outside the limits of his previous habits. Few great inventions, artistic or practical, have emanated from really old persons, and comparatively few even from the middle-aged . . . The period from twenty years up to forty seems to be the most favorable for inventiveness."

Evidence relative to this question of when, during a scientific career, investigators are most productive has been brought forward by Lehman.[1] He examined the records of several hundred noted chemists and the dates of their outstanding contributions. He also studied the most important advances in physics during the past three centuries and the stages of the physicists' lives at which their scientific discoveries were made. Plotting of the average number of contributions each year of adulthood resulted in a graph characterized in both instances by a sharp rise to ages between thirty and thirty-five and then a fairly gradual fall to about the age seventy. So far as I have been able to learn, there has not been a similar study of investigators who have engaged in experimental biology. In medical history, however, there are many examples of important advances made by men before their thirty-fifth year. Laennec invented the stethoscope when thirty-four. Both Long and Morton began the use of ether as an anesthetic when they were

[1] H. C. Lehman, "The Creative Years in Science and Literature," *Scientific Monthly*, XLIII (1936), 151-162.

twenty-seven. Banting was thirty-one when he discovered in-sulin. Ehrlich started his revolutionary work with stains when he was twenty-three years old. Jenner was not yet thirty when he made his studies on vaccination. Semmelweis recognized the infectiousness of puerperal fever at twenty-nine. When Claude Bernard was thirty, he had already started his classic researches on the glycogenic function of the liver. Von Graefe, at age twenty-nine, devised the operation for cleft palate and founded modern plastic surgery. Many more instances might be cited to show that in the years below thirty-five important discover-ies and novel activities are common.

It should be recognized that there is a difference between the amount of performance in the early years of maturity and the ability to continue respectable performance in later life. In fact there is little proof that at thirty-five productive schol-arship is maximal in quality. Lehman found in his study of chemists that some individuals do their best work when they are relatively old, and some do little that is really worth while until they are relatively old. If an individual has failed to make a notable contribution by the time he has reached thirty-five it would be erroneous to assume that he will never make such a contribution. In a study of one hundred chemists recorded as each making one notable contribution, Lehman found that 34 per cent made that contribution after they were forty, 19 per cent after they had passed fifty, and 5 per cent reported their first important research after they had reached fifty-five years of age. One chemist made his single noteworthy contri-bution at the age of sixty-nine! It seems, therefore, that it would be futile to declare that at any particular chronological age an investigator's, or at least a chemist's, scientific usefulness is at an end.

The question naturally arises why statistics indicate a grad-ual falling off in scientific productiveness as the decades pass from the thirties to the sixties. There is little doubt that with advancing age indolence may develop, an indisposition to take the trouble to devise new techniques and to bother with the manipulations which experimental studies demand. Many men, as they grow older, lose the drive which activated them when they were young and were excited by fresh acquaintance with the field in which they labored.

Other reasons for a diminution of productive activity are increasing attention to administrative duties, imposed by the institution which the investigator serves, and involvement in local and national committees and commissions. It is natural enough that when an investigator has entered the later decades of life and meanwhile has gathered experience in various ranges, his judgment should be more and more relied upon. Thirty or forty years ago, in the United States, the older leaders in physiology had all practically ceased personal participation in their science; they were devoting time to public services in which their wisdom was highly valued. One of the first to prove that contributions to physiological knowledge could be continued to the final years was S. J. Meltzer of New York City, who for a long time had shown his deep interest in science by persisting in experimental study while carrying on an active medical practice. Another notable figure who broke the earlier tradition and maintained his investigations up to the end of his life was J. J. Abel, the pharmacologist, of Johns Hopkins University. Still other notable instances of continued and effective productiveness are Sir Frederic Gowland Hopkins, the biochemist at Cambridge, England, who was still engaged in research in his laboratory though over eighty years of age; Pavlov, who was experimenting shortly before his death at eighty-six; and G. H. Parker, the zoologist, who at seventy-six was awarded a prize by the American Philosophical Society for recent significant work on the control of adaptive color changes in fishes.

What conditions favor continued creative activity? Undoubtedly an important factor is good health and a retention of such vigor as leads one to wish to keep a hand in experimental procedures. Another condition is the preservation of a habit of open-mindedness and a willingness to pay attention to novel suggestions which reading or imagination may provide. Variety of early experience is also likely to be favorable, because it offers a diversity of ways in which one may look at a given problem, and also an acquaintance with diverse methods of solving the problem that may make the solution actually tempting. Still another advantageous circumstance is the continued intellectual stimulation which an investigator may have in his associations with eager young men who come to him for suggestions and guidance. All these conditions are helpful in keeping the elderly investigator "outside the limits of his previous habits."

It seems probable that co-ordinated progress in research, progress characterized by a natural development from one group of ideas to another, instead of a flitting from interest to interest in a quite inconsequential manner, is conducive to persistent effectiveness in productive scholarship. In this type of research, as studies advance and new facts are discovered, fruitful ideas accumulate and earlier ideas take on new meanings. As a result, fresh opportunities for exploration are frequently disclosed. The researches which my collaborators and I carried on in the Physiological Laboratory of the Harvard Medical School were of this co-ordinated, progressive character. The studies on digestion went forward from my twenty-sixth year, when I first used the bismuth meal, until I was forty. From forty to forty-six the studies on the bodily effects of emotional excitement were emphasized. Investigations on wound shock (an intrusion due to World War I) took place between forty-six and fifty-one. Interest in stable states in the organism developed between fifty-one and fifty-nine; attention was given to chemical mediation of nerve impulses from fifty-nine to sixty-eight; and after that time an effort was made to complete a series of observations on the effects of severance of nerves on sensitizing to chemical agents the isolated structural elements. The foregoing must be taken as only a rough statement of the distribution of my interests, however, and not as a precise separation of them at the ages which are set down; there was always considerable overlap. Incidentally investigations were undertaken as to the nature of hunger, the nature of thirst, and, in my seventy-first year, on the phenomena of a pace-maker in the rhythmic pulsations of the cerebral cortex. During more than four decades of attention to physiological investigation I was not conscious of any abatement of imaginative insight into problems to be solved or into methods by which solutions of them might be attained. This judgment must be taken with a grain of salt, however, because advancing years may have marred the reliability of my testimony!

There may be a large discrepancy between physiological old age and chronological old age. Some men are old at fifty-five and others are young at seventy-five. As the decades slip by, however, all of us are subject to bodily changes, some obvious and some hidden. Brown spots appear on the face and hands. The hairs grow long in the ears and nostrils, and the eyebrows become shaggy until they may lend a fierce look to the countenance. The skin is less elastic, as is shown by pinching it on the back of the hand and noting a briefly persistent ridge instead of a prompt snap back to the proper level. The "pregnant hinges of the knee," as well as other hinges in our limbs, are not so well lubricated as they used to be. The near point of clear vision recedes until with unaided eyes the elderly person, holding the page at arm's length in order to see it clearly, is bothered by the indistinctness due to distance; caught between these troubles of too near and too far, he moves the page back and forth—as Holmes put it, he has reached the "trombone age!"

Besides these more or less obvious changes there are others, revealed by physiological investigation, that we may not recognize. For example, there is a gradually increasing limitation of the effectiveness of the homeostatic devices which keep the bodily conditions stable. The ability to control body temperature is so much diminished that the old man needs more wraps during the cold of winter, and he hovers near the fire or the radiator as he did not when younger. Also he is likely to find the heat of a summer's day especially uncomfortable; indeed, the death rate from heat stroke rises sharply after the seventh decade of life. Furthermore, the organs which prevent the appearance of acid in the blood—the lungs, the heart, and the blood vessels—perform their functions less efficiently as one grows older. The chest becomes more rigid and thereby lessens the maximal intake and output of respired air; the highest heart rate induced by exercise gradually decreases, and the pumping of blood in a supreme effort is therefore slower with advancing years; and the blood vessels may become hardened and surrounded with obstructive connective tissue. Vigorous exertion, which produces acid and thus interferes with physiological efficiency, cannot be engaged in as it was in youth. The elderly man can look with amusement on the frolicsome and exuberant antics of a young puppy playing around a serene and indolent old dog and can say to himself, "I, too, played like that when I was young, and I was good for not much else. Now that I am old, I cannot be so energetic, but I can be useful to a degree not possible in those early years."

The physiological limitations of old age arise because our bodies are composed of a group of co-operative organs. All goes well as long as each one performs adequately its role in the complex. It is when an important organ becomes impaired and fails to "play the game" that a break occurs. Sometimes the kidneys fail, sometimes the heart, or the stomach, or the lungs; and then the partly broken man must learn to live within his limitations, a course which requires wisdom and patience. He may lead a helpful existence for many years; Holmes's formula for longevity was to have a chronic disease and take care of it. Providentially, as long as the blood vessels of the brain supply that extraordinarily delicate and sensitive structure with an abundant supply of oxygen and sugar, clarity of the mental processes is preserved and pleasant social relations, as well as cherished personal activities, can be continued.

Institutions in which men are employed for a lifetime of service have found difficulty in devising a kind and considerate manner of discriminating between physiological and chronological age. Not uncommonly in universities professors are expected to retire at sixty-five or at some age between that and seventy. This expectation affects both those who are already senescent and those who are still alert. Obviously it is quite appropriate for the senescent; it is often a hardship for those who are still rich in ideas and eager to push forward studies in which they have been engaged. Deep disappointment of active investigators at being deprived of the opportunity to go on with their studies can be avoided, and preservation of the possibility that their labors may still be productive can be assured, if a sympathetic and generous administration provides them with laboratory space where they can satisfy their desire for further attempts at solving problems.

In Harvard University it is well recognized that at the age of sixty-six a professor may voluntarily retire on his pension, or the administrative body may ask him to retire or not to do so. On my sixty-sixth birthday I sent a letter to the President announcing the date and placing in his hands my resignation, to be accepted whenever he might wish. A very gracious answer expressed the hope that I would continue in the services of the Medical School. That proposal was followed by four more years of happy associations. Then, after just fifty years in the University as student and instructor, I withdrew. I could not do so without acknowledging my deep obligation to my alma mater. She had given me every opportunity to learn, to be disciplined in workmanship, to become influential as a teacher, and to engage, with utter freedom, in physiological research. All that I had been able to accomplish I owed to the highly favorable circumstances which the University had provided.

I confess that retirement broke sharply habits established during many decades. There was a mingled feeling of relief and a queer sense of inexcusable neglect when the time for meeting students arrived and I was not there, in my accustomed place. By good fortune, after I had been "on the shelf" for more than a year, a call to be visiting professor at the New York University College of Medicine for three months resulted in my appearing vertical again before a roomful of medical students. I was confessedly an experiment. The object was to test the effect of introducing an outsider into a group of teachers and students, in order to learn what might result. I was not a professor of any particular subject—I was just a professor! Attendance at exercises in medicine, in neurology, in psychiatry, in public health; conferences with a group in therapeutics and talks with young investigators in anatomy, surgery and physiology; lectures to classes and to professional audiences—all these experiences, enjoyed in a most friendly atmosphere, restored relations which had been interrupted and—whatever they may have been to others—they were, to me, very stimulating.

In my lectures to the medical students I restricted myself to accounts of the scientific studies carried on by my collaborators and myself during the previous forty-seven years. As a result I relived my professional career as I first told about the simple primitive employment of the Röntgen rays in physiology, and went on to describe bodily effects of emotional excitement, the mechanisms of functional stabilization in the organism, the chemical mediation of nerve impulses, and recent researches on wound shock and the characteristics of rhythms in the cerebral cortex. The reader will recognize at once that to a great degree that is the survey I have made in the pages of this book. Here again I have relived my career as I have written about it. And now the story is nearly finished.

When I look back over the various stages of my life I remember, as I feel sure many others have remembered, incidents which have revealed how relative are the ages of individuals. In my teens my teachers in the high school, most of them in their thirties, seemed to me elderly persons, to be respected as much for their many years as for their learning. On reaching into the thirties myself I was a beginner in physiology and for the first time attended a meeting of the American Physiological

Society. It was held in Philadelphia, and to the delight of younger members of the organization Dr. S. Wier Mitchell, one of the founders—a medical investigator, an eminent neurologist, a novelist and a poet—was present to talk to us. He appeared to me to be so old as to be almost ancient. And now I find that, at the time, he was not quite my present age! Although I still seem to myself no older than I felt a decade ago I recognize that the changes of senescence have begun to appear and will probably increase until the end. In Dr. Mitchell's words:

> I know the night is near at hand.
> The mists lie low on hill and bay,
> The autumn sheaves are dewless, dry;
> But I have had the day.

# INDEX